# Lean Six Sigma in Sickness and in Health
## An Integrated Enterprise Excellence Novel

**Forrest Breyfogle**
**Arvind Salvekar**

SMARTER
SOLUTIONS

**www.SmarterSolutions.com**
**Austin, Texas**

# Resounding Praise for
*Lean Six Sigma in Sickness and in Health*


"Forrest has done it again! He has embedded a clear description of the simplicity and power of the Six Sigma approach within a warm and human story of likeable people struggling to survive the aftermath of a traumatic car accident. A must read for those who still believe that Six Sigma and statistical methods only help in a manufacturing environment." – Paul Tobias, Statistical Consultant and former manager of the International SEMATECH Statistical Methods Group

*Six Sigma in Sickness and in Health* is a must-read for any healthcare organization! Mr. Breyfogle has a unique way of communicating highly complex, statistical-based methodologies in an easy to read and easy to apply format. The industry leaders of tomorrow will emerge through organizations who adopt and implement these philosophies". - Kelly Ann Shy, MHSM, Administrator, Alamo Maxillofacial Surgical Associates, PA

"I found it mildly entertaining and easy to read and clearly describe the $S^4$/IEE in plain English." - John A. Cramer, CIGNA Healthcare

"The book is written in a style reminiscent of *Zapp: The Lightening of Empowerment*. This style makes the concepts easy to understand, and may be just the ticket for managers who are new to the language." - Pat Korbus, B.S., M.A., Organizational Development Consultant Seton Healthcare Network

# Our Other Books and Publications

*Solutions Manual, Implementing Six Sigma, 2<sup>nd</sup> edition* , Forrest W. Breyfogle III, Smarter Solutions, Inc., Austin, TX, 2004.

*Implementing Six Sigma*, $2^{nd}$ edition, Forrest W. Breyfogle III, Wiley, Hoboken, NJ, 2003.

*Wisdom on the Green: Smarter Six Sigma Business Solutions*, Forrest W. Breyfogle III, David Enck, Phil Flories, and Tom Pearson, Smarter Solutions, Inc., Austin, TX 2001.

*Managing Six Sigma*, Forrest W. Breyfogle III, James M. Cupello, and Becki Meadows, Wiley, Hoboken, NJ, 2001.

*Statistical Methods for Testing, Development, and Manufacturing*, Forrest W. Breyfogle III, Wiley, Hoboken, NJ, 1992.

**Lean Six Sigma in Sickness and in Health**

*Copyright © 2004 by Smarter Solutions, Inc. All rights reserved. No part of this book may be reproduced or transmitted in any form or by any means, electronic or mechanical, including photocopying, recording, or by any information storage and retrieval system, without written permission from Smarter Solutions, Inc. except for the inclusion of brief quotations in a review.*

Printed in the United States
10 9 8 7 6 5 4 3 2 1

**Publisher's Cataloging-in-Publication
(Provided by Quality Books, Inc.)**

Breyfogle, Forrest W., 1946-
    Lean Six Sigma in sickness and in health: an integrated enterprise excellence novel / Forrest Breyfogle, Arvind Salvekar.
        p.cm.
    Includes bibliographical references and index.
    ISBN 0-9713222-1-X

    1. Medical Care--Fiction. 2. Business--Fiction.
3. Six Sigma (Quality control standard) 4. Quality control--Statistical methods. 5. Process control.
I. Salvekar, Arvind. II. Title.

PS3602.R48L43 2004                    813'.6
                                      QB104-700078

# Dedication

To all those who have found or hope to find the change manager within them. Whether you are, have been, or will be frustrated with broken processes in your organization, we hope that this book will lead you through discoveries of successful and profitable change. – F.B.


To my late parents Mahadeo and Nalini Salvekar, who taught all the values I know. – A.S.

# Acknowledgements

The authors thank Solome Skaff who composed the book's storyline around content, Dorothy S. Stewart for her excellent editorial inputs and title idea, Susan Howard, Don Maranca and Mallary Musgrove for final editing, formatting and sending book through the publishing process. We also thank Kim Harrington for her consulting services during the publishing process.

For their voice-of-the-customer input during the development process of our book, the authors thank Bob Ashenbrenner, Paul Tobias, Becki Breyfogle, Carla Breyfogle, Keith Moe, Bill Wiggenhorn, Jerri Saunders, Kelly Ann Shy and Mark Deutch.

For the cover design, we thank Kelli Bienvenu and Shawna Blevins for their creative work.

# Contents

# Preface

Six Sigma is a powerful management initiative that has saved companies billions of dollars over the years. Motorola invented it in the 80's as a quality program, and those trained in Six Sigma later became experts in the tools themselves. In the mid 90's, GE built upon the existing Six Sigma model by assigning trained experts (e.g., Black Belts) to work on projects that were aligned to the needs of the business. Within this Six Sigma initiative, companies defined defect opportunities and then applied both statistical tools and non-statistical tools to reduce process defects-per-million-opportunities (DPMO) rates in order to achieve a sigma quality level of 6, which is equivalent to a DPMO rate of 3.4.

The second edition of our book, *Implementing Six Sigma,* (Copyright © 2003 by Breyfogle, Forrest W.; published by John Wiley & Sons, Inc., Hoboken New Jersey) introduced a Smarter Six Sigma Solutions ($S^4$) Integrated Enterprise Excellence (IEE) approach that takes Six Sigma to its next level. With this approach, Six Sigma becomes much more than a quality program. In $S^4$/IEE, the methodologies of Six Sigma become an integral part of the operations and measurements of a company. The $S^4$/IEE approach is unique in that projects are pulled for creation through performance plan operational hand-off metrics and/or strategic plan objectives, rather than being pushed into the system in order to meet improvement goals that may or may not be beneficial to the overall company.

With this approach, organizations get out of the fire-fighting mode where common cause variability is chased as though it were special cause. An easy-to-read novella, *Lean*

*Six Sigma in Sickness and in Health* illustrates the application of $S^4$/IEE to a health care environment, so that the reader can better visualize its use in situations that may be more directly applicable to them.

This book is not meant as an implementation guide. Rather, it seeks to explain $S^4$/IEE in a thorough but entertaining and easy-to-understand way. For those readers interested in taking a peek at the more technical side of $S^4$/IEE, statistical analyses and technical information have been included in the appendix.

This easy-to-digest format is perfect for executive managers scanning for the right management initiative. This format is also useful in allaying the nervousness (and the accompanying loss of productivity) that middle and lower level managers often experience when a new management initiative is introduced. Armed with the information they'll find here, the implementation experience can be one of confidence, optimism, and new energy for everyone involved. It can create buy-in at all levels and motivate managers to become Champions, Black Belts, or Green Belts, three important Six Sigma roles that you'll become further acquainted with by the end of this book!

Finally, this book (and $S^4$/IEE) is not just for those in manufacturing. The principles of $S^4$/IEE work for all businesses with processes that can be expressed numerically. For example, in this story, $S^4$/IEE is applied to the health care industry – the farthest thing from manufacturing! Yet, hospitals can, and have, saved millions of dollars by applying $S^4$/IEE principles to their industry.

As you read, no matter in what profession or industry you work, you are encouraged to imagine how $S^4$/IEE could help *your* company improve its bottom line and customer satisfaction at the same time. For your convenience, a glossary and list of symbols have been included at the end of this book to define any unfamiliar Six Sigma or $S^4$/IEE terminology. For the reader who is hungry for more, we recommend our book, *Implementing Six Sigma,* which contains all the $S^4$/IEE information your company will ever need – and then some! This detailed, technical, and comprehensive guide has received excellent customer reviews, which can be read on the web by performing a search for "Implementing Six Sigma" at www.Amazon.com. For those who would rather hear it in person, we recommend contacting a consultant who specializes in the $S^4$/IEE methodology.

No matter who you are or in what industry you work, we hope you'll see that with $S^4$/IEE, increasing the bottom line doesn't have to mean cutting jobs or closing plants and branches. This is one management initiative that can save money *and* jobs at the same time!

**Servicemarks**

The phrases 'Integrated Enterprise Excellence', 'IEE', 'smarter solutions', 'satellite-level', '30,000-foot-level' and '50-foot-level' and the logo featuring the words 'smarter solutions' and an upwardly moving arrow are servicemarks or registered servicemarks of Smarter Solutions, Inc. Smarter Six Sigma Solutions and $S^4$ are servicemarks of Smarter Solutions, Inc.

13

# Chapter 1: The Accident

"What a beautiful day," Jorge Santos exclaimed to his wife as he sped along the two-lane highway, one hand on the wheel and one elbow out the window.

"Couldn't agree more," his wife Sandra replied, smiling at his enthusiasm as she looked out onto the passing scenery, "75 degrees, light breeze – a perfect day for golf."

Jorge wrapped her small hand in his and they drove on in silence, appreciating each other and the wonderful day ahead. They had really been living it up the past year or so, Jorge reflected, spending more and more time together. A big part of that credit went to $S^4/IEE^1$. His job as Senior Vice President of Harris hospital had become a lot less difficult and a lot more rewarding since they implemented the Smarter Six Sigma Solutions management initiative. Cost was down and customer satisfaction was up, which made him look great. The smoother running operation also meant he had more time to spend with his wife and friends on the golf course!

On top of all that, his friends had taken to calling him "the Professor" – a title that Jorge humbly accepted as a compliment. It all began when he started casually telling them about $S^4/IEE$ on the golf course over three years ago. Eventually, they decided to push for implementing $S^4/IEE$ at their own companies, and it had been as much a success for them as it had for Jorge. Now they were all reaping the rewards together.

---

[1] Term used within this book to describe the wise application of Lean Six Sigma techniques throughout the whole enterprise of an organization. See preface and glossary for further explanation.

Just then his thoughts were interrupted by a semi truck coming the other way, which blew past them on the narrow highway, rocking the happy couple's car.

Sandra's eyebrows show up, "Holy cow! That was close!"

"Sure was!" Jorge agreed, scowling at the disappearing truck in the rearview mirror. "That guy ought to be more careful. 'Course these old two lane highways are so narrow. You have your seatbelt on, don't you?"

Sandra tugged at the belt around her chest, "Got it. Jorge, look at this next car coming – he's *awful* close, isn't he?"

Jorge saw the car too and Sandra was right – his left tire was practically rolling right down the double yellow line in the center of the two lane highway. It made him more than a little uneasy, so he slowed down and got as far over to the shoulder on the right as he could without letting his tires hit the gravel. The approaching car was a black sedan, and when it was about 100 yards away Jorge saw that it had begun to swerve into his lane a little, then a little more.

Sandra gasped. The rest was in slow motion for Jorge as he watched the approaching car weave violently back and forth, tires smoking. Jorge slowed to almost ten miles an hour and actually pulled onto the gravel shoulder of the road, but the car swerved at them like a heat-seeking missile. The last 100 yards closed in a blurry flash of screeching metal. Jorge caught a glimpse of the driver the final second before impact - it was a woman, middle aged, slumped over the steering wheel, seemingly unconscious.

Jorge leaned back and gripped the wheel as the sedan slammed into them head-on with a horrendous crash, and then everything went black.

16

Jorge awoke to a young woman who shook him lightly by the shoulder, "Are you okay? Mister, Mister, can you hear me?" Jorge realized that his eyes were open long after he opened them. He was in shock. He wondered why the woman's eyes got so big when he first raised his face to her. Why did she cover her mouth like that? The sound of her voice outside the smashed car door window faded away then. Everything became quiet and still. His own heartbeat and breathing were the only things he could hear in the following moments.

The airbag in the steering wheel had deployed during the crash, and now lay deflated in his lap - a thin blanket of powdery white plastic, marred only by a few dark red droplets of blood. The sight of it made him aware that something was running warmly, quickly, down his forehead. He touched his fingers to the wound he found there and winced. Acrid smoke from the airbag deployment filled the air. Voices slowly worked their way into his consciousness.

He looked next to him and saw Sandra lying limp in her seat, seatbelt still secure, deflated airbag rustling against her unconscious form. The airbag lying across her legs was red - very red. A blast of adrenaline washed through his system as he recognized the redness as blood, and concern for his wife overtook everything else. She was unconscious and terribly injured about the head and face. He wasn't a doctor, but he'd worked in a hospital long enough to know that head and neck injuries are the most dangerous. Jorge struggled to free himself from his seatbelt so that he could lean over far enough to check her breathing.

As though from far away, but now getting closer and closer, he heard the woman outside the window pleading with

17

him, "Mister, don't move her! Don't move her! The ambulance is on its way!" He heard the sirens approaching in the distance.

He put his ear to her mouth and could just barely feel her warm breath. He took her wrist in his hand and felt her pulse. She was alive.

"Good," he thought, "that's good," and he assured his unconscious wife, "You're gonna be ok. You're gonna be fine."

A trickle of blood crept into the corner of his eye.

He cursed and looked into the partially shattered and dangling rearview mirror to see how badly he was hurt. That's when he first saw the long, deep gash running across his forehead, so deep that he thought he could see some bone down there...and then he turned white and passed out for a second time. Although he'd worked in a hospital for years, great amounts of blood still made him a bit squeamish.

"Sir! Sir!"

Jorge's eyes flickered as he struggled with consciousness. The first thing he did was look to his right and saw that his wife was not in the seat next to him.

"Where's Sandra?" he asked groggily, still disoriented.

"She's being put into the ambulance," said the paramedic, a large balding man with a grave but compassionate face and a deep, steady voice. He held a compress to Jorge's forehead.

That was when Jorge noticed that his car door had been somehow removed, which was how the paramedic was able to lean over him. Then he noticed the red and white ambulance lights, and the blue and red police lights, flashing dully in the daylight. He realized that he must have lost some time somewhere.

18

In an effort to spot Sandra, he looked past the highway patrol officers looming behind the paramedic, taking notes in small pads, talking on radios. The smell of burnt rubber again filled his nostrils, and the squawk of police radios filled the air. Finally he saw her, just twenty feet from him, on the other side of the tow truck and police cars, as she was being loaded into the back of an ambulance.

"Is she going to be all right?" he asked, attempting to get out of the battered car.

The pear-shaped paramedic held him firmly in place. "Easy," he said, "Not so fast. She's sustained some serious injuries, but she's breathing and she's got a strong pulse. We're taking her to City Hospital..."

"City? No, no...we go to Harris hospital..."

"Sir, Harris is more than a half hour from here. City hospital is only ten minutes away and we've already called it in."

Jorge didn't like it, but the paramedic was right. Time was of the essence. He had an uneasy feeling, though, about going to City Hospital. It wasn't that he'd heard anything that was necessarily bad about them; it was more that he knew Harris was so good, especially after the implementation of $S^4$/IEE. "I want to come with her, in the ambulance."

"You're her husband?"

"Yes."

"Okay. Your head wound looks superficial. You'll definitely need some stitches, but it looks okay. Can you stand?"

"Yes, I think so."

"Okay, take it slow."

The paramedic helped Jorge out of the car. Now that his adrenaline was kicking in again, Jorge felt as though he had just downed an entire pot of coffee. "I'll check you for a concussion in the ambulance, but you seem all right."

"Long as we do it on the way, that's fine by me," Jorge said with determination, and they made their way through the crowded accident scene to an ambulance parked along the shoulder of the highway. Jorge braced himself on the rear ambulance door when he got his first full sight of Sandra on the gurney, IV tubes coming out of her arms, clothes and skin darkened with blood, delicate eyelids closed as in a deep sleep.

He felt the paramedic's firm, strong hand on his back, "You okay?" he asked.

Jorge shook off his fear and nodded sharply, then began to pull himself up into the ambulance.

"Hold on one second, sir," said the paramedic who was already inside and attending to Sandra, "let me just get her locked in before you climb up."

As Jorge waited impatiently, he looked around to see if he could get a glimpse of the driver that hit them. That's when he saw that there was another ambulance on the scene too, parked just past the police and fire truck further down the highway. Its emergency lights were off. Two other paramedics walked towards it, wheeling a gurney with a black body bag on it across the rocky shoulder of the road.

"Is that the other driver?" Jorge asked the paramedic outside his wife's ambulance with him.

The man followed Jorge's gaze to the body bag, and bobbed his head grimly a few times, "Heart attack," he answered, "she was probably gone before she even hit you."

"Okay," the paramedic inside the ambulance waved him in. "Let's go."

Jorge took a deep breath, grabbed the rear door of the truck and pulled himself up.

# Chapter 2: What Bad Processes Mean to Good People

At the hospital, Sandra was unloaded quickly and efficiently by the paramedics and met at the doors by the triage team. Jorge trailed along behind. It had been established in the ambulance that Jorge suffered only from a deep laceration to the forehead, caused possibly by some flying debris during the accident, but there was no concussion. Sandra, on the other hand, was in serious but stable condition.

When the triage team met them at the hospital's emergency entrance, Jorge was relieved. His well-trained eye for emergency room procedure and military-like efficiency gathered that everything was as it should have been...at first.

The on-duty physician and the triage team of nurses hustled Sandra down the hall on her gurney, hovering around her on all sides. As they ran towards the trauma room, they called out her vitals and the doctor ordered medications and gave commands in an urgent, yet controlled voice.

Jorge walked briskly along beside them, "I'm here, honey," he called to Sandra. "I'm right here."

Suddenly, someone gripped Jorge by the arm and pulled him aside.

His eyes locked on the triage team surrounding his wife; in the back of his mind he became cognizant that someone was calling to him, telling him that he couldn't go any further. Actually preventing him from moving forward. The triage team did not stop, and Jorge watched them disappear down the hall, rolling his wife towards what he assumed was the trauma room.

"Sir," came a voice next to him, "Sir, please stop. I need to ask you some questions."

It took some effort for Jorge to peel his eyes off his wife's retreating path, but finally he did. He looked over to see who had him by the arm and met the furrowed, blue-eyed gaze of a strong woman in her mid-forties wearing an all-business expression. It was the triage nurse. Jorge saw that her nametag read Melanie Watson, RN. He stopped struggling against her firm grip. He knew from his dealings with the battle-hardened ER triage nurses of Harris Hospital that he had as much chance of getting past her as he had of winning the Pulitzer Prize for interpretive dance.

"No," Jorge told her in anticipation of her questions, "She's not on any medications. No pre-existing medical conditions, or allergies to any medications. Our regular doctor is at Harris Hospital – Doctor Jack Gray. He has all our records. Um… gosh, I'm having a hard time thinking right now. What else can I tell you that will help?"

"That's enough for now. We can get anything else we need from her records at Harris," she said, handing him a clipboard with the usual litany of insurance forms and liability releases, "but I do have some papers for you to fill out."

He noticed on the forms that there was no place for him to describe the accident, or anything to capture any items from Sandra's medical history that might be of immediate importance to the kind of treatment she'd be given.

Jorge mechanically took the clipboard from Nurse Watson, suddenly uncertain as to whether or not he was still in shock. "But don't you want any information about the accident, or...or any further background information about Sandra?"

"Sir," Nurse Watson said hurriedly as she backed towards the ER doors, "If you'll just fill out the paperwork

22

we've given you, that will be sufficient. We have everything we need to give your wife the best emergency care possible. The best thing you can do for her is to wait and let the doctors do their job. We have a very good team here. Now please excuse me - I'm needed in the trauma room."

Jorge wasn't worried about the quality of their team; he was sure that they were dedicated, caring professionals. It was their *process* that worried him.

"But...what if there was something that...something important that I've forgotten, or didn't know about..." he must have sounded frantic, was possibly even incoherent to some degree. He could read it all over Nurse Watson's face.

"If you think of anything," she told him, "just write it on the back of one of these forms and show it to the nurse at the reception desk. She'll get it to us if it's important."

Jorge simply stared blankly at her in response, all the while thinking "*If it's important?*" Everything his $S^4$/IEE training taught him about the Voice of the Customer went against what Nurse Watson had just said. If there was one business in which the VOC was important in, it was a hospital.

But he let her leave him without further protest, a sinking feeling building in his stomach with every step she took. Oh, how he wished they had been taken to Harris hospital instead. He should have insisted upon it! But it was too late now. Nurse Watson was right. All he could do at this point was get out of the way and let the City Hospital system work. He didn't like it, but it was Sandra's only chance. He tried to be optimistic...

...and quickly failed when he turned and wandered down the hallway towards the hospital ER waiting room.

"This place is a mess!" he thought as he looked around.

23

The bright white tile hallways were lined with stretchers that looked yellowish in the fluorescent light. One of the patients lying there had what looked like a serious head wound. He reached silently, deliriously, for every third person that walked by. The others on the stretchers were unconscious, hooked up to IV's, some moaning in discomfort.

In the waiting room itself, on the two score of blue shell chairs that looked like they were right out of the 1950's, was a variety of patients who had made it to the ER on their own steam. In one corner was a mother with a wailing baby. A college student sat with a compress held to the side of his face, head tilted back and to the left. Another young man sat alone with a blanket around his shoulders, shivering. And there were others, many others: a pregnant woman, a man with a cut leg, and several elderly couples. They weren't waiting patiently either, and had seemingly abandoned, long ago, any pretense of a positive outlook. Most seemed morose and dissatisfied.

Not to mention, Jorge thought as he surveyed the hive of activity around the nurses' station that the staff seemed stressed out and rushed – it looked as if they hadn't planned on being so busy that sunny afternoon, and were understaffed. Triage time was slow, even though some of the nurses were actually running from one task to the next.

Jorge picked a nurse and watched her perform what seemed like one task, yet she had to run twice from one side of the room to the other in order to get some object that was vital to that task. Jorge shook his head slowly. He worried that these small inefficiencies were only the tip of the iceberg, and was now seriously questioning the ER Department's ability to give his wife the best treatment possible.

He shook it off. "Got to stay calm," he told himself.

He re-doubled his efforts to be positive and took a seat closest to the nurse's counter. There was nothing he could do at this juncture to help City Hospital perform its job any better, he reasoned to himself. The system they had was the system they had. He just had to get out of the way and let it work. But underneath that, he couldn't help but think that, as soon as it was safe, he would have Sandra transferred to Harris Hospital.

He filled out the forms that the Triage nurse had given him, writing down everything that could possibly be helpful to the team, and simultaneously cursing the hospital for not running a tighter ship.

He also thought of Sandra, sitting somewhere in an OR prep room, bandaged and probably immobilized, IV tubes coming out of her arms. He wished he could be with her instead of out here in the waiting room feeling so helpless and trying in vain to be positive. Then, over the loudspeaker, he heard, "Trauma Team to OR, Trauma Team to OR."

Uh oh. He knew what that meant and closed his eyes in stolid disbelief. The ER was staffed with only one Trauma Team, he guessed, and they were busy, so they had to page the on-call Trauma staff – and on a sunny Sunday afternoon like today, it was a good bet that at least one of the doctors needed to operate on Sandra was out hitting the links about now. Hadn't he been going to do the same thing himself? He only hoped that they kept another OR prepped and ready to go, so that when the team arrived, all they would have to do is scrub up and get to work.

Jorge finished and turned in his paperwork, then began pacing the hallway. It didn't take him long to realize that he should probably contact family –their son, Michael, for one. He was in Boston doing an internship for a financial company, but Jorge knew their boy would fly home at a moment's notice

25

if he knew his Mom needed him. Then there was his wife's sister, Helen, who lived in town with them but was out of town for the weekend on vacation. Jorge had a younger brother, who lived in Asia with his family, working for a company there, but there was no sense in calling him – it would take him a day just to get here. That was it for close family. Both Jorge and Sandra's parents had passed away years before. He debated whether or not he should call and worry Helen and Michael, but decided that just in case, he'd better call. If he didn't, and something happened…

He walked through the hospital's emergency room and exited the building in order to get some privacy. He then looked up his son's number on his cell phone and hit the speed dial. He sagged when he got the answering machine after three rings. "Mike," he said at the tone, unsuccessfully attempting to keep the worry out of his voice, "it's Dad…"

He paused, cleared his throat. Did he really want to leave this message on his son's answering machine? Finally he just said, "Call me when you get in. Everything is…ok. But… please call. It's important. Bye."

He clicked off the phone, then dialed Helen's number.

"Message L-17," an automated voice spoke after one ring, "the customer you are trying to reach has traveled out of the coverage area. Please try your call again. Thank You."

Frustrated, Jorge clicked off the phone. Should he begin calling friends? What could he tell them? He didn't even know anything about Sandra's condition yet. He decided there was nothing they could really do for him at the moment, except try to console him. He didn't really want to be consoled at the moment, however. He wanted to focus on Sandra, and what he could do to help her. He thought it might be strange, but he didn't want a lot of people patting him on the back and telling him it was all going to be ok right then.

Finally, he decided to try everyone again once Sandra was out of surgery and he knew more. Feeling better with this decision made, he wandered back to the ER waiting room, tuned out everything around him and sank alternately into prayer and deep thought. He did not know how much time had passed when suddenly he felt a firm hand grip him by the shoulder. He came out of his trance and looked up into the clear blue eyes of a woman dressed in a green gown with a green hair cap – a surgeon.

"Mr. Santos?" she asked.

Jorge was afraid, "Yes, that's me," he told her, "Is she..."

"She's stable," the surgeon said, "My name is Doctor Miller, and I'm the trauma surgeon who will be operating on your wife. Her wounds are serious, but she's got strong vitals. That's a good sign. But we haven't been able to operate yet. Our on-duty Trauma Team is operating on another patient right now, so we've paged the on-call Trauma Team and are prepping the OR."

Jorge sighed as his worse fears were confirmed, "How long do you think it'll take to get everything ready?"

The surgeon's eyes were steady, "Mr. Santos, we're moving as quickly as we can, but we have to wait until everything is ready. It shouldn't be long now. I'll send a nurse out to let you know when we've begun operating."

"Ok. Thank you, doctor."

"Hang in there."

The doctor left and Jorge went back to pacing. Fifteen minutes later, the doctor came out to talk to him again. Hadn't she said she would send a nurse?

"Dr. Miller, is there something wrong?"

"No sir, everything is still fine. I just wanted to let you know that the plastic surgeon needs to be paged."

"Great!" Jorge thought. "Another process that hasn't been error proofed."

Dr. Miller went on, "Your wife has sustained some injuries to her nose and teeth," she explained, "and we want Dr. Monk to be there when we operate."

"Okay. How long until he can get here?"

"It won't be long. Don't worry. Dr. Monk is very good – the best. She's going to look ten years younger when he gets through with her."

"If you don't mind," Jorge said weakly, "I'd just as soon have her back just the way she was."

The doctor smiled and gripped him firmly by the shoulder once more, "We'll tell you as soon as we know something," she said. Then she turned and went back though the OR doors.

A new wave of anguish washed over Jorge as he thought about the precious time this new delay would cost his wife. No matter how caring and confident the trauma surgeon sounded, Jorge knew that every minute that slipped by worsened his wife's chances for a full recovery.

Two hours later, a nurse came out of the OR to tell Jorge that surgery had begun, and that he could move to the OR waiting room if he wanted.

Jorge wandered through the hospital hallways, following the colored arrows on the floor that led to the OR waiting room. He found it more than a little disconcerting to be forced to navigate a maze at a time like this. When he finally found it after two wrong turns, he joined the other denizens of the waiting room: several small groups of

28

distressed families who huddled together in the small, blue-carpeted room. A television was on in the corner; some kind of mid-afternoon game show, but no one was paying attention.

The surgery seemed to take forever. During this time Jorge drank coffee and worried about the speed of lab tests and x-rays or if the hastily prepared OR would be properly equipped for doctors to operate. He worried because of the lack of error-proof systems in their process. What if Sandra got the wrong kind of sedation, or blood? Simple but devastating mistakes like that could happen easily when nothing is stopping them. There were even cases of patients having the wrong limb amputated – and how easily something like that could be avoided! In *his* hospital, for example, they simply gave a marker to amputee patients so that they themselves could indicate for the doctors where to cut; and that was just one example of the kind of basic but cost *and* quality effective improvements $S^4$/IEE had led his hospital towards implementing.

Eventually, Jorge was able to calm himself enough to sit down and begin waiting in earnest. Hours later, the trauma surgeon came out to see him. She was still in her gown and cap, mask hanging limply around her slender neck.

Jorge rose to his feet as she entered the room, heart thumping, "Is she all right?"

The trauma surgeon allowed herself the briefest of smiles, "The surgery was successful. She's stable."

"Thank God!" Jorge softly exclaimed, aware that he was being watched by others in the waiting room who might not receive such good news that day.

"Yes," the surgeon replied, "but we're not out of the woods yet. We'll need to keep her for a while. Tomorrow morning the neurosurgeon will look at her head wound, and the cardiovascular specialist will look at her lungs. Also, we need to run some tests. The lab is running under a heavy load today so that could take a while."

"Okay," Jorge nodded, undeterred from taking a positive outlook, "but the prognosis is good?"

"Yes, but I don't want to give you the impression that she's totally in the clear, Mr. Santos. There could be damage that we haven't identified yet. For the moment, things look good. We'll know more in the morning when the specialists arrive. Okay?"

Jorge nodded soberly, "I understand. Thank you, doctor."

He did understand. She was doing her job. She didn't want him to get his hopes up in case something happened, though more than anything he wanted her to declare victory over his wife's injuries. The fact that she would not caused a small bubble of resentment to form inside him, irrational though it might be.

Minutes later he was talking to the PACU nurse to find out where his wife was going to be moved. He was told that he would have to wait until she got a room before he could see her. He was afraid to see her in her wounded condition, but desperate for it nonetheless. At first, the nurse - a very thin woman with a kind, but beleaguered look on her face - wasn't able to give Jorge any information at all because his wife hadn't been given a bed assignment yet. A cup of coffee later, she told Jorge that his wife would be transferred within the hour to room 1215, but that he shouldn't go up there just yet in case something changed.

"Do bed assignments out of PACU change often?" he asked.

"It's happened," the worn-out nurse told him flatly.

And it happened again. Sandra's bed assignment was changed or pushed back three more times in the next forty-five minutes. Jorge was chomping at the bit and seriously irritated through the entire process. Finally, an hour and a half later, Sandra was put into a room for the night.

# Chapter 3: Season of Discontent

Jorge went up to the room as soon as he was given the go-ahead. When he got to the room, his wife had not yet been wheeled in, and so he spent some time with the afternoon nurse, who was to be in charge of his wife, as she prepared the room for Sandra's arrival.

Her name was Nurse Barnes. She was a tall woman with bright red hair done in curls. She made Jorge think of the character "Flo" from the popular 70's sitcom *Alice*. It was about three waitresses who worked in a diner for the tough-exterior-but-heart-of-gold owner named Mel, who was their boss, cook, friend, and sometimes father.. Flo was the sassy one, always telling the customers to "kiss her grits."

"Sugar," she said to Jorge after they introduced themselves, "you have got to be just plum exhausted. I heard they moved her on you three times!"

When Jorge confirmed this, he opened the floodgates for a mini-rant from Flo, "Well, I tell you what, that's hard. Problem is these darn specialists. Oh they're good – when you can get a hold of one. Sometimes we have to put people in beds just because the specialist won't be available until the next day to make the diagnosis – even a simple one! So what happens? Well, I'll tell you what happens: we run out of beds, that's what. Then when somebody like your wife comes along who really needs a bed, we all have to scramble. I tell you, it's a nightmare."

Ten minutes later, Sandra arrived in the room. She was conscious, but very groggy. She was hooked up to IV tubes in both arms, bandaged about the head and face so that only her mouth, eyes, and the tip of her nose were visible. In a way, Jorge was thankful that he didn't have to see his wife's face when she was so badly injured. He didn't know if he could take it. As the orderly and Nurse Flo hooked Sandra up to a variety of monitors, the rhythmically-beeping machines eradicated the eerie silence in the room. Jorge held Sandra's hand, and they whispered to one another for quite some time, as a couple will in that situation.

"I'm tired," Sandra told him, "but don't leave me."

"'Course I won't leave, Sandra. I'll stay right here."

"Did you bring the Chinese?"

"The what?"

"The orange duck," Sandra whispered sluggishly through her bandages with a thick tongue.

Jorge looked up at Flo, "What's she talking about?"

"It takes a while for the sedation to wear off," Flo explained to him in a whisper. "It's normal if she's a little disoriented for a while. Does she like Chinese food?"

"No," Jorge leaned in to the nurse, "that's just it – she hates it! Especially Duck! Gave her food poisoning once."

Flo shrugged and whispered, "I've heard stranger. S'cuse me now a minute, hon."

She moved around to the other side of Sandra's bed and leaned over her patient to introduce herself. Then she said to Sandra, "Can ya tell me if yer in a lot of pain, sweetheart?"

"Not too bad," Sandra answered her, trying to sound courageous.

"You sure you're not just saying that so you won't worry this fellah beside you here? Who is he, anyway?" Flo teased her, "You want me to get rid of him for you?"

"Oh, no." Sandra whispered, and Jorge thought he could see the hint of a smile at the edges of her mouth. "He can stay."

"Well, okay. But you have to promise to tell me if you're feeling too much pain, okay?"

"Yes," Sandra agreed weakly.

"You better promise us that, Sandra," Jorge put in.

"Okay," she said.

Flo smiled, "Good - it's settled then. Well, Jorge, I think she's going to need some rest, so don't keep her up all night, y'hear?"

Jorge found himself smiling now, something he wouldn't have thought possible in such a situation.

A few minutes later, Jorge watched as Sandra's heavy eyelids dropped and she fell asleep. Flo had left, and Jorge was alone with her in the room. He pulled a chair from the corner up to her bedside and turned on the TV to watch their regular Sunday night shows together. He commented on the shows to her as he always did, hoping that the familiarity of it all would make her feel comfortable and at ease in her slumber.

At one point he turned the TV down, took out his cell phone and tried his son Michael again. He wanted to share with someone the news that Sandra was out of surgery and was doing well, but he got the machine again. Before the tone could sound, he disconnected. No sense leaving another message. He tried Sandra's sister Helen again too; got the same message as he had before.

So he gave up and settled into his chair; however, try though he might, Jorge couldn't sleep. He wished the specialists were there to tell him whether or not Sandra was going to be all right – not tomorrow morning, but *now*. He again wished the accident had happened closer to *his* hospital, where he knew and trusted the way that things were done. He reminded himself to keep his anger in check, that it wasn't any doctor's or nurse's fault, but the system they followed that was flawed. He reminded himself that he had probably participated in just such a system, subjecting who knows how many families to this level of frustration at Harris hospital, back before they adopted an $S^4$/IEE approach and changed things for the better.

Now more than ever, he knew the true value of those systemic changes.

# Chapter 4: Buy In

That night, Jorge continued tossing and turning in the uncomfortable chair next to Sandra's bed as he thoroughly examined every conceivable outcome of this present situation. It was a grim reminder of what poor quality meant in a hospital. On the other hand, whether it was a hospital, a restaurant, or a factory, when the quality of a process suffered, you could be sure that somebody, somewhere, was also suffering as a direct result - to a greater or lesser extent, of course. Getting a bad steak at a restaurant was nothing compared to a botched surgery, but neither was desirable. And hey, what about food poisoning? If a restaurant had a poor system for preparing food, someone could get sick. A botched surgery might kill you, but a bad case of food poisoning would make you *wish* you were dead, as Sandra had repeatedly attested during the Chinese Duck incident. Businesses had been sued and gone belly-up over less – the direct result of an incapable process; i.e., a process that does not consistently produce results consistent with specification requirements or customer expectations.

Finally, Jorge drifted into that state of being that is neither sleep nor wakefulness; thoughts swept along subconscious, undirected currents. He settled into one uncomfortable position in the hospital chair and held it, while he drifted back a couple of years, back to when Harris hospital first began considering the implementation of Six Sigma. He remembered the first meeting they had about it, just the top brass. All the VPs were there, including himself. The CEO was there of course, as was the consultant who had been hired to help explain Six Sigma to everyone, and to help the CEO create buy-in from the hospital executives. In his dream, he recalled the meeting perfectly. All the executives seated around the long, oval-shaped mahogany table had only a vague idea of what they were there for. They knew the hospital had to do something to improve efficiency. That was no secret. Jorge knew that a handful of them were more than a little nervous. With the blame-shifting that had been going on within the ranks recently, some wondered if their heads weren't getting a bit too close to the proverbial chopping block.

When everyone was seated, Michael Jefferson, a silver-haired man with a booming voice who also happened to be the CEO of Harris Hospital, called the meeting to order, "People," he began. "Let's get right down to it. This hospital is in trouble – the kind of trouble that can put us all out of a job. Some of you have come to me with proposals for how to fix things, but I have to tell you, I haven't seen anything that addresses the *entirety* of the issues that we face. That's not your fault, and it's not your job to see the big picture. It's my job. So, I've been looking into some things on my own."

Mike, as he insisted everyone call him, made a broad sweeping gesture to his left, where a thin man with glasses sat. Jorge had never seen him before, and, judging by their expressions, the other VPs didn't appear to know him either.

"Oh great," Jorge thought, "another consultant."

"Ladies and gentlemen," Mike announced, "I want to introduce you to Tom Gorman – a specialist in Smarter Six Sigma Solutions, Integrated Enterprise Excellence. They call it $S^4/IEE$ for short, and in case you're wondering what it is, it's the new Six Sigma management initiative that we're considering for Harris Hospital."

The eyes of all the hospital VPs swiveled to Tom, who smiled and waved to the group a little awkwardly in response. One of the VPs sighed heavily.

"I know what you're thinking," Mike went on, raising his big leathery hands in protest to the sigh. "Some of you have heard of Six Sigma before. Often, people think that Six Sigma is applicable only to manufacturing and I have to tell you, I myself was one of those people. However, what I've found out is that this just isn't true. The $S^4$/IEE approach is especially beneficial to transactional applications, such as the medical care industry."

"Now, I've talked quite a lot with Tom about all this, and so far he's impressed me with his ideas for Harris. Of course, you all know, I like to get as much feedback as I can, so I asked Tom to come in and lay it all out for you. And listen, let's face it, whatever we decide to do, you guys are going to be the ones who make it work, so I want you to be real honest about your feelings on this. Is that clear? Good. Tom?"

Jorge and the other VPs again turned their attention to the stranger in their midst. This time, they looked at him a little differently in light of the CEO's introduction. Whatever his "official position" was, Mike wouldn't have brought Tom in to talk to the hospital's top execs if he hadn't already been at least partially sold on $S^4$/IEE himself.

Jorge heard someone at the end of the table clear his throat. It was Bill Burman, VP of Operations. Mike heard it, too.

"Got something to say, Bill?"

"No, well. Not really. It's just...haven't we gone down this road before, Mike? I mean, what about all our efforts with Utilization Review, TQM - the list goes on and on. These new management initiatives come and go, and I hate to say it, but how much do they actually fix? More often than not, they just take one problem and splinter it into several new problems.

Reminds me of that scene in *Fantasia* – you know, with the brooms?"

That got a smile out of a few people at the table, and some of them were nodding their heads too, but this was serious business. Penny Wilkinson, VP of Finance, took up where Bill left off.

"He's right," Penny moaned. "Let's face it. When these things do come along, whom do we put in charge of them? If we're honest, it's the people that we can do without – the most dispensable people in our departments. Am I right?"

Several more nods around the room. That was one thing Jorge thought Harris Hospital had going for it – the execs were all about as honest and straightforward as they could be with one another.

"I hear you," Mike said, not the slightest bit of defensiveness in his tone, "but I'm telling you, this one is different."

Several more light-hearted moans around the room. They had all heard *that* before, too.

"No, people, really," Mike protested, "everything you've just brought up is true, but S$^4$/IEE has an answer to it all. I'm telling you, and I don't want to color your opinions on this one, but I'm excited about this like I haven't been in a long time. That doesn't mean that I don't want your honest opinion on what Tom has to say. If we do go ahead on this, *all* of us have to be on board."

The excitement communicated by their CEO seemed to allay the skepticism of the VPs, at least it did in Jorge for the moment, as he turned his attention back to Tom.

As Mike and the VPs continued to hash their initial feelings out, Jorge leaned back a little in his chair and sized up this new wonder-consultant. The man looked to be in his mid-to-late forties, and Jorge had to admit, the guy just plain *looked* smart. Maybe it was the glasses, or the pocket protector and calculator in his shirt pocket. Maybe it was the shrewdness and self-control in his demeanor – the way he let Mike introduce him and debate the effectiveness of "*another* management initiative" with the executive board without appearing the slightest bit ruffled or getting defensive over S$^4$/IEE when it came under attack. He seemed very professional. Jorge got the feeling that the consultant had been through this a time or two before.

"...anyway," Jorge heard as he faded back into the group's discussion, "we've got Tom here to answer all our questions, so why don't we let him do that? Tom, you've got the floor."

"Hi, everybody," Tom began. "First of all, I'd like to thank you for your time – I know you all have busy schedules."

Polite smiles and nods all around the room.

"Ok then. Well, I think to start off with, congratulations are in order. If you all decide to implement Six Sigma with a S$^4$/IEE approach here at Harris hospital, some of you will become even more important than you already are. Just a minute ago, you were talking about how the people that are assigned to new management initiatives are generally what might be referred to as 'deadweight'. Not so with S$^4$/IEE. Make no mistake about it; those assigned to an S$^4$/IEE team are the best of the best, the future stars of the company. Why? Because S$^4$/IEE saves the company money – big money. S$^4$/IEE team members are highly visible, and because they have total support from the uppermost levels of management, they are given whatever resources they need to implement whatever changes are necessary. That's the way it works, folks. When you're with S$^4$/IEE, you're making big decisions that have a high profile impact on the company bottom line."

Jorge didn't know what he was expecting, but what Tom had just described wasn't it. Jorge was still cynical; but he figured there was no harm in listening, especially if S$^4$/IEE could bring him the kind of recognition that Tom just mentioned. Jorge stole a glance around the room and saw that he wasn't the only one who seemed to be making an effort to keep an open mind.

"S$^4$/IEE folks are given the backing and the proper incentives to get the job done," Tom went on, "but from those given much, much will be expected."

Jorge's eyebrows went up – did he say *incentive?*

Tom smiled, "I suppose some of you are wondering what a consultant like me does in all this, so let me tell you. For starters, I'll set up a steering committee, arrange for the training of the exec team, and help what is known in Six Sigma as the 'Champions' of the Six Sigma team."

There were some strange looks around the room when they heard the title of 'Champion', but Tom blazed over them like Jorge's SUV on a bumpy gravel road.

"It's very important to train internal personnel for the role of Champion. Champions *must* help implement S$^4$/IEE if it's going to be a success. Champions are the people who know this organization inside and out. They're very familiar with all of Harris Hospital's processes, know everything there is to know about the internal politics, how to get changes made, whom to talk to in order to get something accomplished. These are things an outsider can't do effectively."

"Now, get ready for another title that might sound a little unorthodox, because here it comes. In Six Sigma terms, I'm what's known as a Master Black Belt – or MBB."

41

This was a title that Jorge couldn't help but smile about, considering Tom's beanpole frame and slight awkwardness. A look around the boardroom told him that others were similarly amused at this man, who appeared to be as non-threatening as they come, referring to himself as a Master Black Belt.

Tom smiled and held up his hands in protest, "I know, the titles sound a little funny. But, once you understand Six Sigma, the martial arts terminology begins to make sense. The things you're going to be able to do with the hospital's bottom line and customer satisfaction are going to make you feel like the Bruce Lee's of business!"

Mike chuckled and nodded enthusiastically. VPs around the room laughed too.

Tom went on, "I'll be helping Harris to develop their own MBBs from within the company, who will then go on to train internal personnel for the various roles within $S^4$/IEE, and then you will have your own Master Black Belts, and you won't need me anymore."

Jorge's smile deepened in sincerity at that news. "Incredible," he thought, eyebrows going up a notch, "He's actually going to train himself right out of a job! That certainly lowers the threat-level on him, anyway. It's good to know that my job's not in jeopardy."

Jorge took a moment to wonder how much productivity and money Harris hospital had lost in the past when new management initiatives were implemented with no such assurances.

"Until then," Tom continued, "I will be a resource to you. At the lower levels of $S^4$/IEE, I will help teach, coach, and monitor those doing the day-to-day work of the $S^4$/IEE implementation. I'll also train and coach key managers on the finer points of $S^4$/IEE company-wide."

"At the higher levels, I'll help develop your S$^4$/IEE infrastructure. We'll look for new ways of doing things that, on your own, you might not normally be able to see - simply because you've all been in this hospital so long! That's nothing against you; it's only natural that you would become acclimated to this environment. But I have the advantage of having worked with several different hospitals. I can call your attention to their success and failures. There's no reason for us to re-invent the wheel. We can save valuable time by avoiding what we call "companization"; that is, trying to come up with how HARRIS will do the implementation because HARRIS is different. No. Generally, the processes of one hospital will go a long way towards informing the processes of another – just the same as in a factory or a restaurant. My experience will help Harris capitalize on that."

"Finally, when it comes to executing an S$^4$/IEE Project, I'll coach teams to pick the projects that will make the greatest impact on bottom line and customer satisfaction."

Tom paused, letting it all sink in, "Before I go on, does anybody have any questions so far?"

Jorge noticed the silence in the room. Everybody seemed much more positive now.

"Okay then," Tom continued, "now that you know what my job is as a consultant and coach, let me tell you a little more about S$^4$/IEE itself. If you're the kind of person who likes definitions, here you go; S$^4$/IEE is a methodology for pursuing continuous improvement in customer satisfaction and profit that goes beyond defect reduction, and emphasizes business process improvement in general."

"Earlier, someone wondered if efforts in the other management initiatives Harris had implemented were wasted. Not at all. S$^4$/IEE integrates Six Sigma with Lean

Management, Theory of Constraints, Total Quality Management, ISO 9000, Malcolm Baldrige Assessments, and Shingo Prize. Does that about cover them all?"

The room was silent as Jorge and the other VPs struggled to think of an improvement initiative they had tried that Tom hadn't named.

"Okay then," Tom went on, "Now, let me give you a little bit of an idea of what most likely attracted your CEO here to Six Sigma in the first place. Let's start with a brief history."

"The father[2] of Six Sigma was the late Bill Smith, a senior engineer and scientist. It was Bill who crafted the original statistics and formulas that were the beginning of the Six Sigma culture. He took his idea and passion for it to the CEO of Motorola at the time, Bob Galvin. Bob urged Bill to go forth and do whatever was needed to make Six Sigma the number one component in Motorola's culture. Not long afterwards, Senior VP Jack Germaine was named as quality director and charged with implementing Six Sigma throughout the corporation. So, he turned to Motorola University to spread the word about Six Sigma company-wide and around the world. The result was a culture of quality that permeated Motorola and led to a period of unprecedented growth and sales. The crowning achievement was being recognized with the Malcolm Baldrige National Quality Award in 1988."

"That was the beginning of Six Sigma's becoming a dominant force in management culture. Then, in the mid-1990's, Jack Welsh, CEO of General Electric, initiated the implementation of Six Sigma in the company so that the quality improvement efforts were aligned to the needs of the

---

[2] Reproduced with permission, *Implementing Six Sigma*, 2nd ed. Forrest Breyfogle, Wiley, 2003: pp. 4-5.

business. This was a little different from the way Six Sigma had been used in the past. This approach made use of both statistical and non-statistical tools within a structured environment to create a knowledge base that led to higher-quality products developed in less time than the competition. The selection and execution of project after project that followed a disciplined execution approach led to significant bottom-line benefits to the company. Since then, many companies, both large and small, have followed GE by implementing various versions of Six Sigma."

"Now, $S^4$/IEE takes Six Sigma to the next level - from a traditional project methodology to a comprehensive business strategy. There isn't one area of this hospital's business that can't benefit from $S^4$/IEE."

"So, that's the basic history, folks. Just wanted you to know you're in good *company* when you're thinking about implementing Six Sigma."

The VPs all laughed at Tom's lame pun on the word "company".

"Now let me give you a crash course in *how* all these wonderful results are achieved. I won't get too technical because we'll cover all this in detail during training if Harris hospital decides it wants to get on board with Six Sigma."

"The first thing you should know about is the importance of having a reliable system of process measurement. Incorrect measurements lead to a lot of misdirection and wasted efforts; these are called 'fire-fighting' activities that don't fix the underlying system problems. Bad information will force you into a cycle where you're constantly fixing the 'problems of the day.'"

"Implementing a business-needs-aligned functional-hand-off metric system throughout an organization addresses this issue. It is very important that measurements are aligned to the overall needs of the business; this is a structure very similar to that used by GE."

"These metrics are then tracked. If a process is measured and found to be *incapable*; that is, if it doesn't consistently produce what is needed, then our metrics will 'pull' for the creation of process improvement projects. These so-called *projects* will then improve process capability in such a way that problems are less likely to occur in the future. To say it another way, $S^4$/IEE focuses on fire prevention, rather than fire fighting."

"So, what does this functional-hand-off metric system look like? Well, there are three main levels. The first level is known as the 'Satellite-level'. At this level, business metrics, such as profit, are tracked in a time-series fashion, perhaps monthly. These business metrics are viewed as though they are from an enterprise that consists of a system of integrated sub-processes. At the Satellite-level, we're expecting some level of variability. We create 'XmR control charts' to measure whether this variability is common or special cause, which I'll talk more about later."

"The next level down is the 30,000-foot-level. Since the results described in the satellite-level control chart are merely a function of the output of processes that feed into the overall enterprise, the 30,000-foot-level chart focuses on specific processes within an organization. Important outputs to these processes are called 'Key Process Output Variables', or KPOVs. The 30,000-foot-level gives a high-level view of these KPOVs for process or operational metrics."

"Now, when a 30,000-foot-level control chart is in statistical control, the process is said to be 'predictable'. Predictability means that the capability/performance metric of the process from the past can be used to describe what we can expect from the future."

"And the lowest level metric is known as the 50-foot-level. This nomenclature is reserved for KPIVs, which stands for 'Key Process Input Variable'. KPIVs affect the output of a process and are identified through a Six Sigma project. 50-foot-level control charts are used to determine when KPIV levels have changed so that adjustments can be made to these variables, thus minimizing, in a timely fashion, any detrimental affects to the process output level."

Tom stopped and took a big breath. He looked around the room and took stock of his audience. Some of the VPs around the board table took notes, while others seemed thoughtful.

"I know that's a lot of information," Tom added, "and if you don't get it all right away, don't worry about it. Like I said, this is covered in the training. For right now, just know this; the benefits of the $S^4$/IEE approach to implementing Six Sigma is that we focus our efforts on areas that have been defined as key to the success of the business."

Keith Harlow, a broad-shouldered VP who reminded Tom of an NFL linebacker, spoke up for the first time, "Hey, sounds good to me; only how do you make sure that happens? How do you *know* that you're fixing the right thing?"

"Glad you asked that, Keith; just getting to it myself. See, in $S^4$/IEE, projects are 'pulled' for, rather than pushed into creation. I think I may have used that terminology before without explaining it. Pulling for a project means that we don't just sit around and try to figure out what we should work on next as an $S^4$/IEE project. Instead, we have the overall enterprise tell us what needs to get done."

"Okay," Keith said, nodding, "but how does the enterprise tell you what needs to get done? You can't exactly go up and ask it."

A few chuckles around the room.

"Actually, you can," Tom was quick to point out. "There are two approaches you can use. One approach pulls for the creation of $S^4$/IEE projects through organizational strategic plans, while the other pulls for creation through operational performance plan metrics."

"With this second strategy, management measures processes as part of its performance plan in a time-series statistical control chart to see if anything has changed. If a measure is in-control/predictable, management then makes an overall statement about how its overall process is doing. Such a statement might be: 80% of the time, wait time in ER is between 15 minutes and 2 hours, or 10% of the wait times are greater than 2 hours. A goal might then be set in the responsible manager's performance plan that there should be no more than 10% of ER wait times greater than 1 hour."

"Naturally, to achieve these kinds of results, the manager needs to do something different to the system, right? I mean, you don't ask a broken-down mule to win the Kentucky Derby, do you? Typically, the manager will need help; he/she can ask for the creation of a $S^4$/IEE project that addresses this need. And so, to answer your question, the project was "pulled" for creation in this way. Does that make sense?"

"As a matter of fact," Keith nodded appreciatively, "it does."

"Good." Tom smiled at the room. "Once the project is completed, we measure to see if wait time is improved. If it has, then the hospital has improved a process that not only addresses a management performance plan item but also a customer need. Similarly, projects can be pulled for creation through strategic plan requirements. Do you see how that works?"

"I hate to be a wet blanket, coach," Josh Garrison, VP of Shipping said, "but I'm still not sure that I see what's so great about 'pulling' for projects. Pardon me if this is too direct, but so what if some metric tells you to do something – why is that better than listening to an actual person who's experienced in the job he does?"

"I know," Tom sympathized, "it seems that these days people are being replaced by machines more and more. But don't worry; $S^4$/IEE has a system in place to capture the kind of information that experienced folks can bring to the table. I'll tell you more about that in a minute. But now let *me* be direct, and answer your question about the advantage of letting the metrics pull for the projects."

Josh nodded, signaling to Tom that he would be patient.

"The biggest reason," Tom told him straight out, "is that numbers don't lie, get territorial, become tired, bored, or have hurt feelings. I'm not saying that staff does necessarily, but the fact is that numbers and measurements are tangible, while statements of quality or lack thereof are little more than subjective observations, which are poor tools to make significant change in a process. $S^4$/IEE can provide many quantitative numbers that measure quality, like cycle time, defects, rework, etc.."

"That makes a lot of sense to me," Penny Wilkinson from Finance interjected, "I'd rather rely on the numbers to tell me what's working and what's not than be at the mercy of someone's subjective opinion of the department he's been managing for the past 10 years."

At that, Josh opened his mouth to protest, but Penny quickly held up her hands. "I'm not saying that experience isn't valuable, Josh; it's just, sometimes people get so used to their way of doing things that they wouldn't know an innovative idea if it walked up and shook hands with them."

Wry smiles around the table, and Josh reluctantly bobbed his head in agreement. "I guess people do have a way of getting caught up in their work," he conceded.

"And that can be a very good quality in an *employee*," Tom put in, "but in a *management initiative*, objectivity is key. The 'pull' system ensures that the projects a hospital runs will be set up to help it achieve its overall strategic plan. All that translates to bottom-line results."

"And let's not forget," Tom continued, "when you're talking about the kind of results $S^4$/IEE offers, you're talking about breakthrough improvements to the overall system, rather than incremental improvements in its various parts. $S^4$/IEE says, 'Don't fix the problem; redefine the system!' This concept comes in part from a highly- accomplished statistician named W. Edwards Deming who first suggested that *94%* of the output of a person or a machine is a result of the system or process that management has put in place for use by the workers."

"Think about that – 94%! With a number like that, we can't just tell people to work harder and then call it a management initiative. We need to give them the tools they need to work more efficiently. That's why, as your CEO mentioned earlier so correctly, it is an absolute must to have all the hospital's top level guys on board to clear funding and obstructions necessary to significant process overhaul."

"Now, when you're talking about process overhaul, you'd better be darn sure that you have a solid implementation method.   That's why Six Sigma utilizes a structured methodology known as DMAIC, which stands for Define, Measure, Analyze, Improve and Control.   This is the standard Six Sigma project execution roadmap, tried and true.   $S^4$/IEE uses some additional drilldowns, which you will all be trained in, to make it even more robust. Here is a picture of that overall process." (See Figure 1)

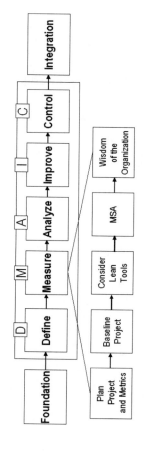

**Figure 1: S⁴/IEE DMAIC Roadmap**
MSA: Measurement Systems Analysis
From *Implementing Six Sigma*, with permission.

Jorge liked the Roadmap. It made $S^4$/IEE less foreign to him. No one liked to move forward with an initiative this significant unless he/she could see what would be required from beginning to end. He imagined the changes possible knowing that the CEO was fully willing to dedicate company resources to the areas a $S^4$/IEE project points them to.

"Sounds great, Tom," said Senior VP Candice Russell as she leaned back in her chair, eyes narrowed in focus on a spot somewhere just over Tom's head, "but how long before we can expect to see results?"

"Ah yes, results," Tom smiled, "my favorite topic. The reason being, $S^4$/IEE develops an infrastructure that produces fast results. A typical project lasts 6 months and can save hundreds of thousands – while costing only a fraction of that to implement."

Tom paused and waited for the statement to sink in as Mike looked up and down the boardroom table over his glasses to see the look on everyone's faces. Jorge knew that at least his own eyebrows went up some. He didn't have to calculate the savings just a few projects could create to see why Mike was so willing to spend the hospital's money on Six Sigma.

"Excuse me, coach Tom," Penny Wilkinson from Finance spoke up again, "but just because upper management gets on board with this, won't there be some anxiety a little farther down the ladder? Have you taken into account the loss of productivity cost associated at lower levels when coming up with these numbers?"

"I have," Tom assured her confidently, "and I can tell you that what we've found is that, unlike some other management initiatives, Six Sigma projects are actually good for company morale across the board! Team members like the power and responsibility; they make real change within their company and like the recognition. And because they are in control of how things get done, $S^4$/IEE team members 'own' the project more. They pour themselves into it, take responsibility for it."

"Interesting," Penny said thoughtfully, "but what about employees who aren't on the $S^4$/IEE team?"

"Current employees whose job descriptions change as a result of an $S^4$/IEE project will be re-trained for their new roles whenever possible; compared to layoffs, it's better for morale and for the customers. Also, from a bottom-line perspective, it's faster and cheaper."

"I tell you what I like about it," Mike spoke up, "and Tom here hasn't talked about this yet, but there's something in Six Sigma called 'the Voice Of the Customer.'"

"Ah yes," Tom said, "the VOC. I was getting to that."

"Sorry to interrupt," Mike apologized, "but I like this part! So far, Tom here's been telling us all about the monetary benefits, but with liability claims in the hospital business, we've got to keep an eye on customer satisfaction, and $S^4$/IEE strives for 100% customer satisfaction. It's like they say, 'If you want to know somebody's opinion, all you have to do is ask.' Well, $S^4$/IEE asks. I like that. I think businesses lose that simple concept sometimes, when it can be to their benefit to remember it. It's not all about having a warm fuzzy heart for people either, because good service is just good business."

"I'll give you just a simple example from my own life," Mike went on. "Geneva and I have what we call 'Sandwich Night' at our house, something we still hold to from back in our college days together when we were broke. I always make the sandwiches for us. Once we started making a little more money, I went out and bought fancy, expensive breads, meats, and cheeses for Sandwich Night in order to spice things up, thinking Geneva would like it. Well, she never complained, so I just kept on going out and buying the fancy meat and cheese and breads all the time. I have to tell you, it was tough keeping up with it, week after week. We spent a lot of money, too, on all those fancy sandwiches."

"Then one day, Geneva came up to me and said, 'Michael, you know what? I don't mean to criticize, but I would like it if you would just make me a plain old ham and cheese on Sandwich Night from now on, like we used to have. Although, if you cut from corner to corner once in a while, instead of just down the middle all the time, it might be nice.'"

Everyone around the boardroom table chuckled respectfully at the story. Jorge figured that everyone knew Mike was trying to charm them all on the $S^4$/IEE concept, but no one seemed to mind. Charisma was a good quality to have in a CEO.

"Wait," Mike went on, "the real kicker was when she added, 'Of course, if *you* want to keep eating all those fancy sandwiches, you go right on ahead, but I just want something simple.'"

The chuckle around the room rose again.

"Can you believe it? All this time I'd been running to every deli in town just to please her, and she didn't even want it to begin with. But I never asked her, so how would I know? I just assumed. Meanwhile, I'm basically engaged in the kind of fire-fighting activities Tom described earlier – running from one deli to the next looking for new things to bring home, thinking I'm solving the problem when really I was just stuck in a process that was incapable of satisfying my customer."

"That's a great example," Tom commented. "This is the kind of low-hanging fruit that the VOC can lead you to. The same thing is true for the voice of the front line workers –

called the Wisdom of the Org. (short for Organization) and this speaks to Josh's earlier comment. Staff is often aware of simple corrections to a process that can be made easily and quickly if only someone would ask."

"Paying attention to the VOC and the Wisdom of the Org. are great diagnostic tools that dramatically improve your problem-solving capabilities. And then, once the problem is diagnosed after examining this and other kinds of data, the metrics will 'pull' for the projects that need to be run, and numerical values rather than subjective values will define project goals…"

Jorge went to a few more high-level meetings with Tom Gorman. At each meeting, there were fewer and fewer questions that searched for a weakness in the Six Sigma concept. More and more, the questions became exploratory of the $S^4$/IEE implementation methodology. Jorge was reminded of the time his own father had given him his first Swiss Army knife. He'd spent hours examining all of the different blades and tools, imagining the endless list of scenarios for which each one of them would come in handy. Once he was thoroughly familiarized with it, he put it in his pocket and carried it everywhere. In much the same way, when the series of Six Sigma meetings with Tom had ended, the VPs at Harris Hospital had a new tool in their pocket.

# Chapter 5: Roll Out

A long steady tone from the pulse monitor sounded in Sandra's room. Jorge bolted upright in his chair, his mind fuzzy from lack of sleep. A spasm caught hold of his back, the result of trying to sleep in such a cramped position in the uncomfortable hospital chair. At Harris, they had small cots so that family members could stay with a loved one in the hospital for an extended period with a little more comfort and dignity in an otherwise difficult situation. Customer satisfaction went way up. People wrote letters, thanking them. All a direct result of the VOC.

But these thoughts were far back in his consciousness and fading quickly, mere remnants of the waking Six Sigma dream he'd been in only moments before. He stood stiffly, slightly bent, as Flo rushed into the room, but before she could even make it to Sandra's bedside, the long, unceasing tone of the heart monitor blipped back into a normal rhythm. Jorge's own heart began beating again, too.

"What happened?" Jorge asked Flo as he took his wife's hand and held it, "Is she all right?"

Flo was unperturbed as she examined the readouts of the different monitors Sandra was hooked up to.

"Seems fine now, honey," Flo assured him. "That happens sometimes. Some people just have an irregular heart beat once in a while and it sets the machines off."

"Are you sure that's what it was?"

"Well, all her readings are stable and normal now. Just to be sure though, we'll have the doctor come in and check on her when he does his rounds, which shouldn't be long now. What about you - you all right, sugar?"

Jorge nodded, stroked his wife's hand, face filled with worry and relief.

"Can I get you anything?"

"Um...No..." then, gripped by a muscle spasm in his back, he added, "actually, you don't happen to have a cot on hand, do you?"

"A cot? No, we don't, but that sure would be handy around here. That's a pretty good idea."

"Thanks," Jorge said wryly, rubbing his back with one hand.

Flo misconstrued his tone and looked hurt. "I can get you a blanket and pillow," she offered.

"That'd be nice, thank you," Jorge answered her with a warm smile to make amends. He hadn't meant to take his frustrations out on her – having her as a nurse was the best thing he and Sandra had going so far at City Hospital!

A few moments later, Flo came back with a blanket and pillow for Jorge, and he apologized once more to her. He then set himself up again in the hospital chair right next to Sandra's bed. Soon, he began to get sleepy, lulled by the now steady and reassuring rhythm of his wife's heart monitor.

However, even with the blanket and pillow, the chair was still uncomfortable. To make things worse, he was now afraid to even let go of Sandra's hand as he tried to get back to sleep. He lay there, one hand under his cheek, the other draped across Sandra's bed. He dreaded the muscle spasms in his back that were sure to seize him the next time he tried to stand up.

"Darn chair," he grumbled to himself, "Got a cot? No, but what a good idea! Glad I could help you out...hmph."

Uncomfortable as he was, however, he still managed to fall asleep. When he slept, he dreamed again of the Six Sigma implementation at Harris hospital. It was natural that he would, considering how quality systems, or the lack thereof, had suddenly become very important to him - maybe more important than they had ever been.

Slowly, he drifted back to the never-never land of Six Sigma, his dream picking up about three months after the initial buy-in by the exec team, when the CEO called a series of larger meetings. The first was a Leadership Meeting with Mike and all the VPs, but it also included the Deputy Directors and Managers. The circle of those being brought into the Six Sigma fold was expanding! Tom Gorman was there too, and that's when Jorge first realized that part of Tom's job, which he hadn't mentioned before, was to help Mike and the execs create buy-in throughout the company.

Tom went through a lot of the same information that he had during the meetings with the exec team. This time, it was the Deputy Directors' and Managers' turn to fire off questions, and the VPs helped Tom field them. This was the first tangible sign to the lower level managers that the entire exec team was on board with Six Sigma, and their resistance to the initiative disintegrated quickly. By the end of the meeting, the decision was made to tell everyone that Harris Hospital was implementing $S^4$/IEE. Mike was happy, Jorge and the other VPs were happy, and everybody started shaking hands. Before long, the company was buzzing with the news.

That was on a Monday. By Friday, an even larger meeting was called in what was known as "The Big Room" where all staff-wide meetings were held. Everyone who was at the previous meeting was there, but also present were several high-performing staff members from Nursing, Laboratory, X-ray, Patient Financial Management, the Emergency Department, the Operating Room, and Materials Management.

Tom was also there, but this time, he wasn't the one doing the talking.

It was Mike, the CEO, who got up behind the podium first, "Thank you all for coming," Mike said into the microphone.

The room quieted down.

"I know there's been a lot of talk in the halls this past week, and I'm sorry to have kept you all waiting so long, but we needed to dot some i's and cross some t's. So, the big news is that Harris Hospital is going to be implementing a Six Sigma management initiative known as Smarter Six Sigma Solutions, Integrated Enterprise Excellence - S⁴/IEE for short. Here to explain any questions you might have is Tom Gorman."

Jorge watched as Tom took the podium and the rank and file of the staff shifted uncomfortably. Sensing the nature of their discomfort, Tom went into his Six Sigma apologetics, letting them all know that their jobs were safe, but that their roles within the company might be changing.

"The first thing you need to know about the changes that are coming is that within Six Sigma, there are various roles. These roles are called Executive Champions, Champions, Master Black Belts, Black Belts, and Green Belts, and I would like to give you all a brief description of them this morning."

The crowd chuckled. How often Tom must have to endure that, Jorge thought. This time, however, the S⁴/IEE consultant went right over the interruption without pausing enough even to take a breath. Jorge reasoned that since the decision had been made to implement at the highest levels, Tom must have figured that the staff would get used to their new titles in time, so that there was no need to dally by coddling them along. It was more important for Tom to convey the staff's new roles to them. Jorge liked this guy – even in his speeches he was as efficient as possible!

"The role of the Executive Champion," the coach continued, "is to motivate others toward common vision, to set the standard for the team, ask the right questions, and always, always use $S^4$/IEE tools in day-to-day operations. Executive Champions are visible, and will give a short presentation that precedes each new $S^4$/IEE training wave. They will also attend project completion meetings conducted by their $S^4$/IEE team and stay involved in the $S^4$/IEE implementation."

"Champions - they help the Executive Champions on the Steering Committee determine what gets done. They remove barriers to success, like making sure your regular duties don't interfere with your new $S^4$/IEE duties. They also help manage incentive programs with the Executive Team – so be nice to them!"

Everyone laughed.

"Seriously, though," Tom went on, holding them off with one hand raised, "the Champions are the ones who communicate and execute the $S^4$/IEE vision. They drive and communicate results, approve completed projects, and perform several other important duties."

"Black Belts. Black Belts have one job, which is to complete the project given to them. They can do this, because they have the full support of the higher-ups to give them whatever they need to get it done. They are the ones that take $S^4$/IEE Projects off paper and into the real world. They are the talent – this is their opportunity to be recognized. If they do their job right, they will give the company a very significant return on investment, and that's never a bad thing for somebody's career."

"Depending upon the situation, Black Belts can be in their role anywhere from 2 – 3 years running different projects. Some, who like working in their Six Sigma role, may be selected to become Master Black Belts which, as I have mentioned on previous occasions, is what I am. Unlike my job as a consultant, however, the Harris people who are trained to become MBBs will eventually take over my job in this hospital, while other BBs who complete their projects successfully might get promoted in their regular job."

"This is why I cannot stress enough to the future Champions in the audience to pick your best people to become Black Belts, rather than the ones you can do without. Six Sigma BBs will most likely be on track for promotion if they run successful projects."

"Likewise, you future Black Belts out there, you should know that if you are picked, it's because you're viewed as having fire in the belly and good team-working abilities. You're thought of as someone who can multi-task and get things done on time. Your involvement in Six Sigma is a compliment to your abilities."

"Finally, we come to the Green Belts. Green Belts help Black Belts with their projects. Think of them as part-time Black Belts who work at improving process that they are directly involved with. They help implement Six Sigma, but still perform some regular duties as well."

"Now, if any of you have any more specific questions about what your roles will be, don't worry. It will all be covered in the training, which I'd like to tell you just a little bit about today."

"Typically, there are four weeks of training spread out over four months. The training covers the five phases of a Six Sigma Project, which are **Define**, **Measure**, **Analyze**, **Improve** and **Control,** otherwise known as **DMAIC.** Six Sigma teams will be trained for one week on the first phase, then will spend the next month executing what they learned – see, right out of the chute the teams will be making real decisions with their new knowledge. This is done for practical reasons. It ensures that the team has really learned the material before moving to the next step, because they will actually be using the knowledge to affect real change within a real business setting. This way, you *have* to learn the material."

"During training, some of you will learn things you already know, but everyone will learn something new. That, I can guarantee you. Of course, during training you will not be expected to do your regular duties and Six Sigma work at the same time. If you all will look at page 2 of the materials that were handed out, you'll find a sample training agenda, where references are made to sections of *Implementing Six Sigma*, the seminal reference material for the $S^4$/IEE methodology (See Glossary and Symbols for description of topics).

# Black Belt Training: Week One
# Define and Measure Phase[3]

1. Introductions and $S^4$/IEE definition of workshop projects – 2nd ed. Chap. 1
1. Overview of traditional Six Sigma – 2nd ed. Chap. 1
2. Benefits of an $S^4$/IEE implementation – 2nd ed. Chap. 1
3. $S^4$/IEE infrastructure – 2nd ed. Chap. 1
4. Theory of constraints (TOC) and project selection – 2nd ed. Chap. 45
5. $S^4$/IEE project execution and integration with Lean – 2nd ed. Chap 44
6. Project COPQ/CODND analysis and project selection – 2nd ed. Chap 1 & 52
7. Define phase deliverables – 2nd ed. Chap. 1
8. Team effectiveness: Forming within orming model – 2nd ed. Chap. 53
9. Project application exercise
10. Voice of customer (VOC) – 2nd ed. Chaps. 2 & 13
11. Measurements to reduce fire-fighting – 2nd ed. Chap. 3
12. Sources of Variation and Sampling Variation – 2nd Ed. Chap. 3
13. Introduction to Minitab and measurements – 2nd ed. Chap.3
14. Process flowcharting – 2nd ed. Chap. 4
15. Project application assignment
16. Basic tools for working with numbers – 2nd ed. Chap. 5
17. Normal distribution and Six Sigma metrics – 2nd ed. Chap. 7
18. Probability plotting: Distribution fit and capability/performance assessment – 2nd ed. Chap. 8
19. Control charts: 30,000-foot-level measurement alternatives – 2nd ed. Chap. 10
20. Process cap./process performance metrics for normally dist. & attribute data - 2nd ed. Chap 11
21. Creativity: Shifting perspectives – 2nd ed. Chap. 54
22. Crafting insightful metrics – 2nd ed. Chaps. 9 & 11
23. Lean implementation within $S^4$/IEE – 2nd ed. Chaps 1 & 44
24. Project application exercise
25. Basic tools for working with ideas – 2nd ed. Chap. 5
26. Project management (PM) – 2nd ed. Chap. 52
27. Effective presentations (Part 1)
28. Example project report out
29. Wrap-up

---

[3] From www.smartersolutions.com. Copyright Smarter Solutions Inc., reproduced with permission.

# Week Two
# Measure (Con't) and Analyze Phase

1. Week 2 Kickoff: Review, exercises, and discussion
2. Control charts: Alternatives and rare events – $2^{nd}$ ed. Chap. 10 (Part 2)
3. Process capability/performance metric: Non-normal data – $2^{nd}$ ed. Chap. 11 (Part 2)
4. Lean 5S (sort, straighten, shine, standardize, sustain) – $2^{nd}$ ed. Chap. 44 (Part 2)
5. Cause and effect matrix – $2^{nd}$ ed. Chap 13
6. Failure mode and effects analysis (FMEA) – $2^{nd}$ ed. Chap. 14
7. Sampling distributions – $2^{nd}$ ed. Chap. 7 (Part 2)
8. Hypothesis testing – $2^{nd}$ ed. Chap. 16 (Part 1)
9. Confidence intervals – $2^{nd}$ ed Chap. 16 (Part 2)
10. Measurement systems analysis (MSA): Gage R&R cont. data – $2^{nd}$ ed. Chap. 12 (Part1)
11. Project application exercise
12. Probability – $2^{nd}$ ed. Chap. 6
13. Non-normal and attribute distributions – $2^{nd}$ ed. Chap. 7 (Part 3)
14. Team effectiveness: Storming within orming model – $2^{nd}$ ed. Chap 53
15. Visualization of data using Multi-vari chart, box plot and marginal plot – $2^{nd}$ ed. Chap. 15
16. Inferences: Continuous Response – $2^{nd}$ ed. Chap 17
17. Inferences: Attribute (pass/fail) response – $2^{nd}$ ed. Chap. 18
18. Comparison tests: Continuous response – $2^{nd}$ ed. Chap. 19
19. Tapping creativity – $2^{nd}$ ed. Chap. 54
20. Comparison tests: Attribute (pass/fail) response – $2^{nd}$ ed. Chap. 20
21. Project application exercise
22. Effective presentations: Vocal variety
23. Example report out (Part 2)
24. Wrap-up

# Week Three
# Analyze (Con't) and Improve Phase

1.  Week 3 kickoff: Review, exercises, and discussion
2.  MSA for attribute gages and non-destructive testing – 2nd ed. Chap. 12 (Part 2)
3.  Variance components – 2nd ed. Chap. 22
4.  Correlation and regression – 2nd ed. Chap. 23
5.  Single factor one-way analysis of variance (ANOVA) – 2nd ed. Chap. 24
6.  Two-factor (two-way) ANOVA – 2nd ed. Chap. 25
7.  Multiple regression – 2nd ed. Chap 26
8.  Project application exercise
9.  Benefiting from $2^k$ design of experiments (DOE) -- 2nd ed. Chap 27
10. Understanding the creation of full and fractional factorial $2^K$ DOE'S – 2nd ed. Chap. 28
11. Facilitating effective teams: Norming within orming model – 2nd ed. Chap. 53
12. Planning $2^k$ DOE's – 2nd ed. Chap 29
13. Design and analysis of $2^K$ DOE's – 2nd ed. Chap. 30
14. Project application exercise
15. Experiment traps – 2nd ed. Chap. 3
16. Effective presentations (Part 3)
17. Example project report out
18. Wrap-up

# Week Four
# Improve (Con't) and Control Phase

1. Week 4 kickoff: Review, exercises, and discussion
2. Variability reduction through DOE and Taguchi considerations – $2^{nd}$ ed. Chap 32
3. EVOP and other DOE considerations – $2^{nd}$ ed. Chap 31
4. Team evolution: Performing within orming model – $2^{nd}$ ed. Chap. 53
5. Change management – 2nd ed. Chap. 51
6. Response surface methodology (Overview) – $2^{nd}$ ed. Chap 33
7. Five-step MSA – $2^{nd}$ ed. Chap 12 (Part 3)
8. 50-foot-level control charting and deception of AQL – $2^{nd}$ ed. Chap 10 (Part 3)
9. Short run and target control charts – 2nd ed. Chap 34.
10. Project application exercise
11. Three-way, CUSUM, and zone charts – $2^{nd}$ ed. Chap 35
12. EWMA/EPC (Overview) – $2^{nd}$ ed. Chap 36
13. Pre-control charts: Application and possible deception – $2^{nd}$ ed. Chap 37
14. Control plan, poka-yoke, and realistic tolerances – $2^{nd}$ ed. Chap 38
15. Reliability testing/assessment (Overview) – $2^{nd}$ ed. Chap 39
16. Non-repairable device reliability evaluation and Weibull distribution – $2^{nd}$ ed. Chap 41
17. Pass/fail functional testing (Overview) – $2^{nd}$ ed. Chap. 42
18. Lean workflow improvement and $S^4$/IEE measurement/integration: $2^{nd}$ ed. Chap. 44
19. TOC workflow management: – $2^{nd}$ ed. Chap. 45
20. Process modeling
21. Triz for idea generation (Overview) – $2^{nd}$ ed. Chap.
22. Project application exercise
23. Design for Six Sigma (DFSS) overview – $2^{nd}$ ed. Chaps 48-50
24. Application examples that combine tools uniquely and/or smartly – $2^{nd}$ ed. Chap. 43
25. Effective presentations (Part 4): Inspire your audience
26. Example project report outs and final report
27. Advanced tools for Master Black Belts
28. Wrap-up

"Workshop attendees find the cross referencing of book chapters to workshop topics very beneficial in the training. Also, project-application exercises drive home real-life application of the statistical and non-statistical techniques, which might seem initially applicable only to manufacturing situations."

"Your initial projects will take about six months to complete. Remember, you don't have to do it all alone. You have the support of VPs and even the CEO to implement necessary changes. With this kind of back-up, nothing is beyond your reach..."

# Chapter 6: Training

Jorge woke up with the words, "Nothing is beyond your reach," still echoing in his mind. He forgot where he was for a moment, then looked to the right and saw Sandra. She looked peaceful, which Jorge took as a reassuring sign. He stood up and stretched, gave her a light kiss on her bandaged cheek.

"You're going to be just fine, kid," he whispered to her.

A grumble from his stomach reminded him that he hadn't eaten since he and Sandra had breakfast that morning – wait, scratch that, he thought, noticing the wall clock which read past 2 am – make that *yesterday* morning. For Jorge, a man who had always enjoyed a healthy appetite, going this long without a meal was rare.

He checked his cell phone to see if there was a message from Michael, but there was nothing. He became somewhat annoyed wondering where their son could possibly be at this hour. Of course, it was Saturday night, and Michael was a young man. He was probably out on the town somewhere, enjoying the city's nightlife, blissfully unaware of his mother's accident. No, he reasoned, if the boy hadn't called by now, he wouldn't hear from him until tomorrow morning at the earliest. So, he resigned himself to getting through the night under his own steam.

He stepped outside Sandra's room and tried to spot Nurse Barnes out at the nurse's station, but didn't see her anywhere. The halls were brightly lit even though it was so late at night, which somehow unsettled Jorge – reminded him that things weren't normal.

He approached the counter and spoke with the nurse there, a middle-aged man with brown hair, "Excuse me," Jorge

69

asked him, "did Nurse Barnes sign off for the night? My wife is in room 1272."

"Yes sir, she's gone for the night. I'm Cliff."

"Hi, Cliff, Jorge Santos."

"Good to meet you, Jorge. I'll be taking care of Mrs. Santos tonight. I looked in on you earlier, but you were sleeping, so I didn't want to wake you."

"Oh," Jorge said, suddenly feeling a little guilty for falling asleep in such a situation. "Yes, I'm not usually up so late."

"Hey, you've got to rest," the nurse replied. "Have you eaten?"

"No, actually…"

"There's a vending machine down the hall with snacks and things. Complimentary coffee, too."

"Is there a cafeteria?"

"Yes, but it doesn't open till 5 a.m.."

"Oh."

"Have a cup of coffee or something. Sandra has had a quiet night since I came on; her signs are strong. I understand there was a brief episode earlier?"

"That's right. Her heart monitor went off for about five seconds. Scared me half to death."

"Well, the doctor came by while you were sleeping, and…"

"The doctor came by?"

"Yes, we didn't want to wake you."

"But…I was hoping to have a chance to talk with him, hear what he had to say…"

"Don't worry; he said to tell you that she's recovering well. He thinks the episode earlier was nothing to worry about; people have irregular heart patterns all the time – it's just that

70

she happened to be hooked up to a heart monitor when it happened."

What Cliff said made sense, but still, he would have liked to have been able to ask the doctor some questions. Again, he felt guilty for falling asleep.

"It's okay," Cliff offered, seeing the worried expression on Jorge's face. "The specialists will be here this morning, bright and early. They start their rounds at 5:30 am."

That was only a few hours away.

"Thanks," Jorge said, brightened somewhat by the news.

"Don't mention it," Cliff said good-naturedly. "Now, go eat. If any doctors come by, I promise to send someone down the hall and let you know."

Jorge thanked Cliff again, checked in on Sandra who was still sleeping peacefully, and then went down the hall to find the vending machine. He hoped they had snack cakes or mini-donuts or something. That and a cup of coffee sounded pretty good right then.

He found the vending area, in a well-lit alcove off the main hallway. He peered in through the glass of the vending machine and there they were – both snack cakes *and* mini-donuts! He poured himself a cup of coffee and then took out his money for the machine. The snacks were $2.25 each, but the smallest bill he had was a 5.

"Well," he thought to himself in feigned disappointment, "Guess I better just get both of them – no sense in changing a 5 dollar bill."

He slid the bill into the machine and pushed the button for the snack cakes first. The spindle holding the cakes spun, but didn't spin far enough, and the cakes didn't drop.

"Hey!" Jorge said aloud.

He slapped the glass a little, then nudged the machine a bit, hoping to shake the cakes loose from the spindle. They didn't budge. He stared into the vending machine glass at the cakes, defeated, as the words "Key Process Output Variable", or KPOV for short, sprung to mind. Actually, it didn't surprise him that much that a Six Sigma term would be so prominent in his thoughts, considering his dream and the situation he and Sandra were in.

He chuckled a little that Six Sigma was even applicable to his experience at a vending machine. But then again, it was an output to a process, was it not? Indeed, the situation fit perfectly, since KPOVs can be described as the outputs of a process that are considered important, whether they are transactional, manufacturing, or development. These too can be tracked at the 30,000-foot-level, for the purpose of separating common cause variability from special causes, and pulling for the creation of a process improvement project whenever improvements might be needed.

Whether Jorge received, or didn't receive his snack cakes, would be an example of one of the KPOVs a vending company might have. The process that went into getting those snack cakes into the machine at the hospital didn't matter to Jorge, the customer. What mattered was that he *received* them once he paid his money. He didn't even much mind having to buy two different products just so that he didn't have to walk around with a pocketful of change. It would have been nothing more than a comforting indulgence in a bad situation. But now, he had to push the snack cake button again, just to make the spindle turn another notch so that he could get the snack that he had already paid for once. That was just plain annoying – and expensive. Even though the snack cakes and coffee hit the spot, he doubted that he would return to that vending machine.

Of course, he reflected further as he wandered back to Sandra's room, Six Sigma also taught that you had to be careful how you collected data. How samples were drawn made a big difference in the way you read a control chart. When collecting data, the approach Jorge's team used to implement $S^4$/IEE back at Harris Hospital taught that an infrequent sampling/sub grouping of the process should be used in order to draw accurate conclusions.

To continue with the vending machine scenario, Jorge imagined that a 30,000-foot-level control chart for a vending company might measure the overall defective rate of all machines in the hospital or even a larger region. An infrequent sub grouping/sampling plan for this 30,000-foot-level chart might include plotting the failure rate ratio of all these machines either daily or weekly. In this type of data, the centerline of the control chart would be an estimate of the process capability/performance metric not only for the past, but also for the future. That is, if on the average, 10% of the people had a problem in the past when they wanted to get a drink from a vending machine, then Jorge would expect a similar percentage of problems in the future. For this 10% problem, Jorge would then need to determine the COPQ/CODND (Cost Of Poor Quality vs. Cost Of Doing Nothing Different), which would include lost sales.

Collectively, the organization would then look at all its opportunities for Six Sigma projects. If the vending machine issue ranked high relative to other areas of the business, Jorge would then see reason to take this on as a Six Sigma project. A Black Belt with his team would then look at the system collectively using a project execution roadmap to determine

73

where the biggest opportunity was. Jorge imagined that this investigation might lead to the removal of problematic machines, modifications to the loading procedures for the machines, and/or more convenient change-making machines. He theorized that more convenient change-making machines were a possible solution, since a lost sale could occur in a situation in which someone who has a $5 or $10 bill might not want to buy a $1 item and get his change back in quarters and dimes.

Jorge's thoughts floated once again to the $S^4$/IEE implementation at Harris Hospital's Emergency Department. One KPOV they had tracked was patient wait time. Another KPOV they tracked weekly was the percentage of erroneous medications. The data was collected daily and examined over a period of several weeks, with these metrics later going into the managers' performance plan.

Examining the data in this way, the differences between time of day, shift, etc., were not as much a factor in the overall output; it was what they called "noise" to the system. The results of causal analysis for variability reduction and overall improvements to the process steps that drove these KPOVs allowed Harris to make some high-impact changes to the system, causing both the patient wait time and erroneous medication rates to drop significantly within 6 months.

Jorge made it back to Sandra's room with his coffee and $4.50 snack cakes and waved to Cliff at the nurses' station as he went by.

"All's quiet," Cliff called softly to him.

"Thanks!" Jorge said, feeling reassured as he re-entered room 1217.

He greeted Sandra with a light kiss between the bandages over her eye, then sat down in the chair next to her bed and turned on the 24 hour TV news channel. The sound came out of the little box speaker on the cord hanging from the side railing of Sandra's bed. They were talking about some court case on the news that Jorge was interested in. They had some legal experts who kept disagreeing with one another. What would Six Sigma do with lawyers, he wondered? Jokingly, he answered himself that perhaps they would be labeled as an "incapable" process that needs a lot of process improvement work!

He flipped around the channels some, grinning to himself, but nothing was on. He went back to the news where the legal experts were still bickering. His mind, bored with the proceedings, picked up his thoughts on KPOVs where they had left off.

Instead of KPOV terminology, some Six Sigma folks, he reflected, use the terminology Critical to Quality (CTQ). However, he'd heard it said that the *Quality* word often turns people off – partly because Quality is such a nebulous, subjective term. What is Quality? The question forces the creation of a "defect definition", which winds up taking all the Six Sigma team's time, and when the company is demanding improvements, on-time delivery is a KPOV for the Six Sigma team, too! Also, there have been many "quality" programs inside companies that have not been very successful in many people's eyes. What Jorge's team did with $S^4$/IEE at Harris was much more than a quality program!

That's why with $S^4$/IEE, "CTQ" as the driving metric is downplayed and, instead, "KPOV" is emphasized. At this stage of the $S^4$/IEE process, tracking KPOVs is a numbers focused activity, where subjectivity is removed from the equation.

Managers and their staffs can have a status meeting weekly to discuss their 30,000-foot-level KPOV metrics, which would tell them how their processes are performing. With this approach, they start getting out of the fire-fighting mode of attacking common cause occurrences as though they were special cause events. Out-of-control conditions would identify when something has changed within the overall process. When process improvement is desired, management can ask for the status of $S^4$/IEE projects that are aligned with improving the metric. Then, as a step within the project execution roadmap, it would solicit VOC and the Wisdom of the Organization inputs so that valuable experience from dedicated employees is taken into consideration when the $S^4$/IEE team deduces what it should do next.

Each metric treats the process or enterprise that consists of many processes as a whole, rather than as separate compartments, which makes managers better able to distinguish between what are called "common cause" and "special cause" issues. Plain old common sense tells us that when measuring a variable over time, we will not always get the same number for each time period, be it day-to-day, week-to-week, or month-to-month. So, if nothing unusual occurs within a specific time period, we call that "common cause" variability.

For example, at Harris, tracking the number of ER visits hourly showed a lot of within-day trends that were dependent upon the *time* of the day. However, when they tracked the mean and variability in a number of ER visits *weekly*, they typically saw only those types of differences that could be expected between weeks – that is, "common cause" variability.

Occasionally, there was a "special cause" in the number of ER visits. Once, for example, there had been a major snow storm that resulted in an increase in accidents for that week.

Now, if they had been doing only point estimates of common cause variability – that is, giving each day equal weight in deciding the needs of the ER department, then the changes they would be led to implement would have had little impact on the overall future process output. After all, there's not a snowstorm every week, so they would have been preparing the entire ER on the basis of an event that only happens once or twice a year!

That's why 30,000-foot-level XmR Control Charts were so valuable. A control chart of individual values is typically referred to as an I chart or an X chart. A moving range chart often accompanies these charts; hence, the designation I-MR or XmR chart. The MR chart is a control chart that typically tracks the moving range of adjacent data points. When data was examined over time, common and special cause variability could be determined, and noise to the system could be disregarded. This chart was also sometimes created using sample data. For example, the length of stay (LOS) for someone was randomly selected daily and plotted on an XmR chart (See Figure 2). From this chart, it was noted that the emergency room LOS process was predictable, since all data points were within the upper and lower control limits and there were no trends in the data. From this plot, it was estimated that the average emergency room LOS was 265 minutes. However, the managers at Harris needed to remember that if a process was not in control, they would need to identify and resolve special cause issues.

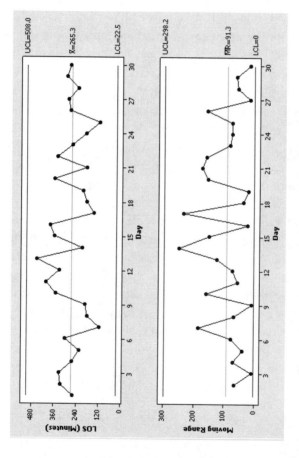

Figure 2: XmR Chart of Length of Stay (LOS)
in Emergency Room for One Random Sample Daily

78

When a process exhibited only common cause variability, data points fell between the upper control limit (UCL) and lower control limit (LCL), which are determined mathematically from the data; i.e., without specification limits. For this situation, a process is said to be "in control" or "predictable." That is, you could be pretty sure about what that process will do in the future unless something changes. Data from a predictable process could then be combined collectively in a non-time series dot plot format, which illustrated the range and frequency of sampled responses from the process (See Figure 3).

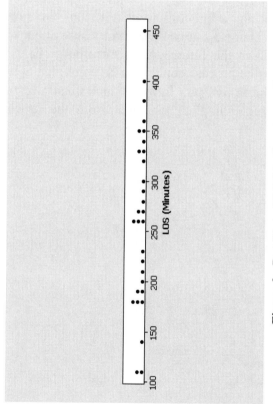

**Figure 3: Dot Plot of LOS in Emergency Room**

80

A tool that quantifies variability better than the dot plot is the probability plot (See Figure 4). From this plot, Harris's $S^4$/IEE team estimated that 80 percent of Length of Stay (LOS) occurrences were between 155 minutes and 337 minutes. This estimate was then used to project future LOS occurrences, assuming that the process remained at the same statistical control level. If this was not the level of response that was desired, then something needed to be done differently; i.e., results from process measurements could pull (used as a lean term) for the creation of an $S^4$/IEE project.

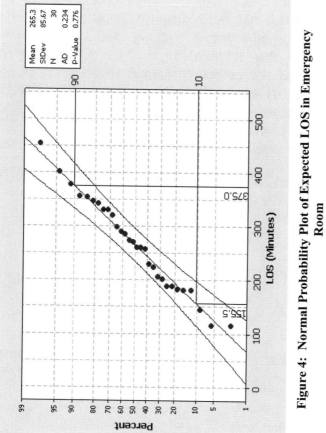

**Figure 4: Normal Probability Plot of Expected LOS in Emergency Room**

Jorge's $S^4$/IEE reverie was interrupted when, on TV, the legal experts took a break for a commercial. It was a woman mopping her kitchen floor, very happy about the way it shined after she was done.

"I didn't even have to scrub that hard!" she told the camera. "New and Improved Glow really works!"

"New and Improved," Jorge mused aloud to Sandra. "Just another way to say, hey, we know our product was junk before, but we made it better now, so try us again! I wonder if they used Design of Experiments (DOE) techniques to create their product so that its performance didn't depend on the techniques people used to actually apply the product."

Jorge had watched the cleaning crew at Harris and had wondered if the product performed consistently no matter if it was applied to their new or old tile, or whether the variation in amount of product that they mixed with water and variability in product application techniques made a difference. Somehow, he doubted that the "Glow" company was so rigorous in its pursuit of data to qualify its "new and improved" claim.

His wife didn't respond, but he went on talking to her anyway. "At least they're willing to change something that doesn't work. You'd be surprised how many won't. Or maybe not, judging by the way you grip a golf club!"

Jorge always enjoyed chiding his wife about the way she gripped her golf club, stubbornly resisting all efforts of others to correct it - despite the horrible slice it gave her. However, since Sandra couldn't really appreciate the humor, it wasn't as fun.

"Have to remember to save that one and use it on her when she gets better," he asserted to himself in an effort to keep from becoming depressed by the situation. Then he continued his S$^4$/IEE thoughts – this time to Sandra aloud. He thought it would be good for her to hear his voice.

"Anyway, sometimes a process does not have a satisfactory level for its process capability/performance metric. When that caused the metrics at Harris to pull for a project, we tweaked the process to try and make it better. 'Course, when you're executing an S$^4$/IEE project, you don't just go around randomly changing things. What you do is, you select tools that will lead you to better understanding of the process and what might be done to improve the process. In other words, you identify the KPIVs that can affect the KPOVs."

"See, when KPIVs are controlled, error-proofed whenever possible, then we can reduce the variability of the KPOVs. Now, I know… I know what you're thinking," he held his hands up to his peacefully resting wife as though trying to keep her from overwhelming him with questions, "but it's not always as easy as it sounds. Sometimes KPIVs are hard to find – actually, finding them is kind of like a murder mystery where the defective tries to determine 'who dunnit.' After we determine who dunnit, we might either need to control the identified KPIVs or redesign the process in some way so that we get the desired KPOV level. See, you didn't know that your husband was a Sherlock Holmes of sorts, did you?"

Jorge was beginning to enjoy this little monologue with his wife. It relieved some tension, at least.. Maybe he could talk to her enough about Six Sigma that she'd wake up and tell him to be quiet, as she had been known to do when he got too carried away on the subject. He just wanted to hear her voice – he knew it might be selfish, but he missed talking to her!

"What's that, sweetheart? You want an example of a KPIV that might affect a KPOV? Well, I'm glad you asked. One example, just off the top of my head, is that some medications are unavailable more frequently than other medications. This would be a KPIV to the KPOV of turn-around time for medication. Simple, huh?"

"Okay, so, moving right along, after we determine all the KPIVs to a KPOV, the first thing we want to do is try to make the system error proof to the impact of the KPIV. For example, in the KPOV 'turn-around time for medication' which I just mentioned, we wanted always to have medicine on stock when we needed it, but we didn't want to have to increase the amount of inventory overall. So, what we did was, we cut a deal with a supplier in order to get them to open an outlet next door to the hospital. This way, they acted like our own private medication warehouse, only we didn't have to pay a dime! And, incidentally, this little arrangement turned out to help lots of other ailing processes throughout the hospital that we weren't even aware of."

"Anyway, after this change was installed, we tracked the availability of medications at the 50-foot-level using a frequent sampling plan so that when something changed, we would know it, and we could stop or adjust the process before it produced excessive non-compliant product – in this case, untimely medicine delivery. So far, things have been great."

"Then there were other times when an examination of KPIVs and the overall process revealed to us that a process needed to be changed in certain areas so that it became more robust to input levels. Levels that were sometimes very high, and sometimes very low. You see, this is not much different from the floor cleaning process with this new and improved cleaner."

"Um, Jorge?"

Jorge turned towards the door to see who had interrupted his discourse to find nurse Cliff standing in the doorway, looking at him as if to assess his sanity.

"Everything all right?" Cliff asked slowly.

"Sure," Jorge said, flushing a little, "I was just, you know, talking to my wife. Think I read somewhere that if they hear a friendly voice it helps to um... bring them around again."

Cliff nodded, "Yes, that's true. Usually though, people talk about more personal matters."

Jorge laughed a little at himself, "I suppose so, but Sandra's used to me talking about this stuff, and she hates to be patronized. Don't want to get too mushy on her."

"Of course," Jorge added, suddenly wondering just how strange it was that he should be talking aloud to his wife about Six Sigma in the middle of the night, "I guess I might be a little over-tired at this point."

"No," Cliff assured him with a warm smile, "I'm sure you're fine."

Then, in the awkward silence between Cliff and Jorge, a weak voice from the bed said, "Hey, don't you patronize him."

Jorge turned around in shocked surprise, and Cliff walked past him and approached the bed, suddenly all business. Sandra was awake again.

Jorge took her hand, emotions welling up inside him. She still seemed groggy, but she was looking right at him through her bandages.

"Well, hello, sleepy-head," he smiled warmly at her. "Good to see you again."

Sandra gave him a feeble smile.

"Hi, Sandra," Cliff said, "How are you feeling?"

She smacked her dry mouth and said, slowly, "You mean aside from my whole body hurting worse than childbirth? Not bad."

Jorge chortled.

"Well, well, a comedian," Cliff said approvingly, "that's good. You'll need a sense of humor when I ask you to try and sit up for me in a few hours."

Even in her weakened condition, head wrapped in bandages, Sandra was able to send her husband a look that indicated that Cliff was out of his mind.

"Sit up?" she repeated in groggy disbelief.

Jorge sighed, knowing that what Cliff suggested was the best thing for his wife.

"Sorry, hon," he told her, "it's the way they do it now. Used to be they wanted you to rest after surgery for days. Now they want you to get up and get moving about eight or so hours after surgery."

Sandra fuzzily protested that was the stupidest, most unnatural thing she'd ever heard. During her slow, deliberate rant Cliff took some readings off the machines and added them to her chart while Jorge watched.

"Looking good, huh?" Jorge asked Cliff as he wrote, elated that his wife was awake and coherent once more, and showing quite a good deal of vigor, too.

"Not too shabby," Cliff said with guarded optimism, "We still have to see what the neurosurgeon and the cardiovascular specialist say in the morning, but she's lucid – that's a good sign. Of course, even if everything checks out tomorrow, she'll still take a while to heal."

Jorge agreed and tried to keep his hopes and expectations under control. Who knew what the doctors would say in the morning? Anything was possible. The agony of limbo set in once again.

After Cliff left the room, Sandra said, "I'm so tired, Jorge, I can barely keep my eyes open. I think I'll rest a little more. I'm going to be fine, though; don't worry. I'm in good hands."

"Sure you are," Jorge agreed, though inside he winced. "Go ahead and rest a little."

Jorge reached down and stroked her hand. He wanted to touch her face but the bandages prevented him.

Changing the subject, Sandra asked, "What were you talking to me about before?"

"Oh, nothing. Just some Six Sigma."

"I heard you," she said, her eyes fully closed now.

"You did?"

"Mm hm. Tell me some more."

"What do you want to know about?"

"Tell me about…the *tools* you use."

"You mean the Six Sigma and Lean tools that Black Belts use to process data?"

"Yes," Sandra said, "those are the ones."

"Well," Jorge said, speculating that his wife was half-humoring him to take his mind off her injuries, and half just wanted to hear the sound of his voice. Nevertheless, he obliged her request, "since you asked… there does happen to be quite a number of different Six Sigma and Lean tools to pick from. It's interesting actually. Different tools are used to collect different kinds of data. Of course, you've got the 30,000-foot-level XmR chart and process capability/performance metrics, your Dot Plot, Probability Plot, Scatter Plots/Regression, Chi square analysis, Design of

Experiments (DOE), Robust DOE, and a variety of Lean tools …that's just to name a few….Sandra?"

She appeared to be asleep again already. Jorge smiled and without letting go of her hand, he slowly eased himself down into the chair beside her bed.

"Why did you stop talking?" she said, catching Jorge by surprise and startling him a little.

"I thought you'd fallen asleep!" he said.

"Huh uh."

"Oh, well, okay. Should I keep talking then?"

"Mm hm."

"Okay. Why don't I tell you about how a Six Sigma team goes about picking the right project?"

"Sounds juicy," Sandra replied drowsily.

"All right then, here goes. Once upon a time, as they say, Tom, the consultant, asked us how we thought we ought to decide which project to run. So, someone suggested that we create a list and then choose projects from the list. A lot of people agreed that it seemed like a good course of action, but I wasn't too sure. When I voiced my hesitation, you'll be proud to hear, Tom asked me why I disagreed."

"Well," I told him, "I just thought that you were supposed to line up your projects with the overall strategic plans of the hospital. So, shouldn't we take a look at those first?"

"Good, Jorge," Tom told me, "$S^4$/IEE tells us that instead of focusing on subjective ideas, we can work down from the hospital's overall strategic plans. That way, we run the projects that will have the most impact on helping Harris execute those plans. Later, we'll want to put KPOVs with 30,000-foot-level metrics into people's performance plans, since these metrics address internal supplier-customer handoffs that are aligned with the overall satellite-level metrics of the organization. With this approach, people will be asking for the creation of Six Sigma projects since they know that the only way to meet their performance goals is to change the way things are done, and they will need help accomplishing this. "

"Great job, sweetheart," Sandra commented from the depths of her pain medication. "You were always such a good student. Always with the right answers in class."

"Thanks," Jorge beamed. Then excitedly he went on, "Later, the Wisdom of the Organization told us there was room to improve and standardize procedures in the OR, which would help Harris achieve its goal of improving the hospital's bottom line. So, we looked at the metrics and decided what to do. Once we implemented a few standard, efficient procedures in the OR, the hospital was able to use it more frequently, which increased revenue."

"But let me give you another example. Another goal of Harris' overall strategic plan was increasing customer satisfaction. In that case, the VOC told us that the biggest complaint customers had was spending long periods of time in the waiting room. So, we looked at our data, tweaked the system in order to handle it, and dropped the average waiting room time over 20 minutes. Customer satisfaction rose dramatically, and we got lots of comments about it."

"Before we made all these changes, of course, like I said, we looked at our data and we examined the operational metrics in a strictly statistical control chart fashion, using infrequent sub-grouping/sampling procedures. In both cases, the process we were examining was in control and predictable, but it simply wasn't giving us the level of performance we needed. So, with this objective, no-nonsense data to back up the Wisdom of the Org and the VOC, we created a project to impact our metrics. That is to say, we decided that it was worthwhile to do something about the problem by changing the system."

"Yep, Tom really did his job well when he taught us to create performance metric plans at the 30,000-foot-level that were aligned to the business metrics. Our Black Belts tracked the whole organization as a system of processes where typical day-to-day perturbations were just viewed as noise to the system. We had high-level operational metrics that covered defects, waste, cycle time, days sales outstanding, customer satisfaction, on-time delivery, and inventory. I tell you, we had it all covered. Then, when we needed to decide which projects to run, we let the numbers help us discover where to look."

"If our 30,000-foot-level metrics revealed a process that had major common cause variability and was consistently missing its specification limits, our Black Belts would label the process capability/performance metric 'unsatisfactory'. If we decided to run a project to fix the process, everyone at the hospital would have been made aware of the 30,000-foot-level metric, and the effort the hospital was making to improve it. Then, the 'murder mystery' would be on! We'd drill down until we found exactly what our KPOVs were, along with the KPIVs that affected them."

"Take the medication error rate that I was telling you about before. We found at the 30,000-foot-level the process did not give us what we wanted. Then, we found that a certain type of medication had the highest error rate. So, then we tracked the error rate for that specific medication at the 20,000-foot-level. Eventually, we closed in on our problematic KPIV, which turned out to be bad handwriting and a lack of information. So, in order to fix this, we redesigned the medication order sheet, which improved the process. This was demonstrated when the 20,000-foot-level control chart changed to a new level of performance (See Figure 5). For this failure rate response we can estimate directly from the 20,000-foot-level control chart that the frequency of failure of approximately 50 per 1000 patient days was reduced to about 11 per 1000."

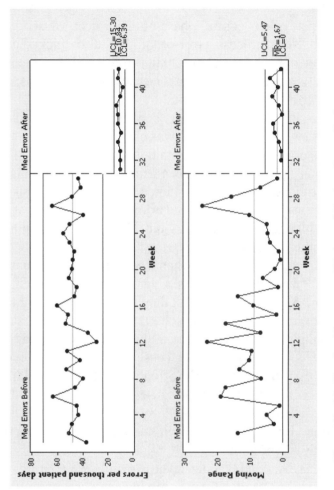

**Figure 5: Medication Errors per Thousand Patient Days (Before and After Improvements)**

"As part of our control phase of the project, we worked to make the entry process error-proof. We also tracked the medication errors weekly at the 20,000-foot-level and placed the specific requirements for this metric in the responsible manager's performance plan …Sandra? You asleep?"

Jorge leaned over to her bed from his chair and determined that this time, his wife was clearly asleep.

He stopped talking then, and his mind drifted. The murder mystery metaphor he'd been using conjured up images in his mind of Elliot Ness and his famed band of crime fighters, closing in on members of organized crime, digging them out of their shady hideouts. Sandra was out like a light and didn't protest as Jorge indulged himself in the fantasy.

Years ago at Harris, when they had first initiated $S^4$/IEE, there were many processes that were in sore need of improvement. Some might say that they were out of control but that was not true. The control charts with infrequent sub-grouping/sampling clearly indicated that the process was in control; that is, it had no special cause conditions. However, the process was just not capable of consistently giving Harris the desired output. Hunting root causes in the processes that affected the KPOV output using a systematic approach had been exciting. Fixing them had been satisfying, like locking up Public Enemy #1 for good.

At Harris, 30,000-foot-level metrics were used to determine that the hospital's most pressing need was improving the Emergency Department. 60 percent of the hospital's business came from the emergency room, and the ED system was problematic. In this case, the operating room systems, revenue cycle, medications errors, and the supply chain had all been suspect.

They tested these issues against the Voice of the Customer just as Mr. Ness would question someone who might have information about a crime. There were two witnesses: the internal customers and the external customers.

The internal customer testified that what had them all mucked up were delays admitting patients to nursing units, re-work in physician orders, turf wars, a lack of customer orientation, specialists who weren't on duty at the right time, a slow admit process, gaps in the scheduling, and the fact that it seemed like there was never enough staff on hand to handle the work load.

Then it was the second witness's turn, the external customers. They testified to the need for quick and cost-effective health care solutions, better and more timely information from the care givers, and better customer orientation.

Yes, Jorge nodded shrewdly to himself in thought, the case wasn't yet closed on these culprits, but now that they had been identified, shutting them down for good was just a matter of time. When they ran a project to impact these issues, they could know for sure that they weren't just going to be fire-fighting, or working a low priority problem. They were on to something that would make a definite impact on the hospital's bottom line and customer satisfaction.

TQM, Utilization Review, Scientific Problem Solving Methodology, Benchmarking...left to themselves, none of them took the broad-based approach of $S^4$/IEE. Jorge harrumphed at the thought of their inadequacy and the memory of all those quality improvement efforts that had come and gone. Using them to solve a problem was like Elliot Ness going after Al Capone armed with no more than a cap gun.

# Chapter 7: Define

At 3:30 a.m. when Cliff came into Sandra's room again, Jorge was watching an old Hitchcock thriller, *North by Northwest*, on the hospital TV.

"Hitchcock, huh?" Cliff asked, stopping to watch for a moment on his way to Sandra's bed.

"Yep," Jorge said, "thought it might take my mind off things. I'm not as much of a fan as Sandra, though. She can watch Hitchcock all day."

"And you can't?"

Jorge shrugged, happy to be talking about something that he and Sandra did together, "Well...sometimes it seems a little hokey. I mean, *The Birds*? Come on."

Cliff laughed, "I like your attitude, Jorge."

"Thanks," Jorge replied, "but I wish I could do more."

"You can," Sandra said, suddenly awake again. "You can get me a drink of water. I'm so thirsty."

Jorge practically jumped he was so surprised. "Will you quit doing that?" he protested to his wife.

"Doing what?" she protested weakly.

"Waking up all unexpected like that."

"Well, I heard you badmouthing Hitchcock and couldn't let you get away with it."

"She's tough, huh?" Cliff said to Jorge.

"You have no idea," Jorge responded.

"I'm sorry, dear," Sandra said to Jorge, "but could I have something to drink?"

"Better make it ice chips for now," Cliff warned, "water might make her nauseated right now."

"That's fine," Sandra said, "I'll take anything."

"I'll go get you a cup of ice; be right back," Cliff said, and he left.

"Well, won't be long now until the doctors are here," Jorge told Sandra as they waited, "Soon as they clear you, I'd like to have you transferred to Harris."

Sandra winced as she tried to shift in the bed. "Do you think that's necessary?"

Jorge quickly leaned over her to help adjust and fluff her pillow so that she would be more comfortable, "Well, I'd just feel better at Harris, knowing how smoothly things run there, knowing the doctors and everybody – you know."

He didn't want her to worry about all the things he knew could still go wrong before she checked out of City Hospital, but he couldn't help but worry himself. When a process capability/performance metric was poor, mistakes could easily happen, and he knew that Sandra might become one of them if they waited around too long.

"Well, if you think it's best," Sandra said, trusting her husband's opinion. "Do you think they'll ask me to stand up when we get to Harris?"

"'Fraid so."

"Oh, nuts."

A moment passed, and then Cliff returned with the cup of ice and handed it to Jorge. Sandra opened her mouth, and Jorge slipped an ice chip in between the bandages.

"Better?" Cliff asked.

"Mmm," Sandra said.

"Don't give her too many. Three should be plenty for now, if she wants that many. She can have more in a little while, okay?"

"Got it; thanks, Cliff."

"Just hit the button if you need me."

"Will do."

He left the room, and Jorge and Sandra were alone again.

When she was finished with the first ice chip, Sandra asked, "So, how long did you talk until I fell asleep?"

"A long time. Do you remember what I was talking about?"

"Not really. I just liked listening to your voice."

"Thought so. Want to hear some more of it?"

"How else am I going to fall asleep?"

"I'm flattered."

Sandra closed her eyes. "I'm waiting," she said.

Jorge chuckled. He really thought she was just delightful.

"Well, if you'll recall," he began, "I was telling you about how we used the Wisdom of the Organization and the Voice of the Customer, in combination with our functional-hand-off metrics, to define the various systemic problems we had at Harris. And as you also recall, I'm sure, in Six Sigma, Defining the Problem is the first step in solving it."

"Ah yes, that's right," Sandra said.

"Tom, our $S^4$/IEE consultant, taught us in our training to pick projects that were fixable, important to hospital success, measurable in their impact on the bottom line, scoped properly so that the team wouldn't become overwhelmed, able to be completed in six months, and able to be supported by the data we collected."

"So, what did you pick?"

"Wow, you haven't fallen asleep yet?"

"No. But wait, I have a question. Didn't you say before that $S^4$/IEE taught you to pick one thing to fix at a time?"

"So you *were* listening!"

"It must have soaked in to my subconscious. Well, what was the first project you ran?"

"The *first* one? Emergency Department throughput. We did our training on that one. It was the lowest-hanging fruit we could find with the biggest payoff for the hospital. Then we moved on to medication error reduction, reduction of accounts receivable, and reduction of inventory."

"How long did they all take?"

"Less than six months each – remember, that was one of the criteria for selecting them?"

"Oh yes, sorry, *Professor*," she said, sarcastically invoking the title his old college friends had given him.

"That's okay, Mrs. Santos, I'll let you take the make-up exam later on in the semester."

"You're too kind."

"Not at all. Actually, once the Champion, Black Belt, and team all agree on the gap between the process output and the expectations of the process customer, things really start to move. Their single-minded focus fuels the project; that's why it's critical for them to all be in agreement."

"But how do you get them all on the same page?"

"Good question. You don't do it with a lot of subjective personal opinions that are guided by ego and self-interest. You do it with numbers and facts. One thing you can do is what's called a 'Cost Of Poor Quality (COPQ) vs. the Cost Of Doing Nothing Different (CODND)' analysis. This then helps you determine how projects are selected and executed. However, there are projects that are beneficial which do not have bottom-line hard benefits. An organization that is rolling out $S^4$/IEE might choose the categories of bottom-line hard-dollar benefits, cost avoidance, lost profit avoidance, productivity, profit enhancement and intangibles. Too bad I don't have the tables we used at Harris so I could show you."(See Table 1) Jorge stopped talking and leaned over Sandra's bed. Her eyes were closed and she was breathing normally.

"Sandra?" he whispered.

No answer. She had zonked out fast this time! Satisfied that she was asleep, he got up and strolled over to the 12$^{th}$ story hospital window, looking out into the early morning darkness. He clasped his hands behind his back as he watched intermittent bursts of traffic roll down the highway visible in the distance.

"One more hour," he thought.

It seemed like an eternity.

**Table 1: Project Benefits**

From *Implementing Six Sigma*, 2$^{nd}$ edition, with permission.

-Bottom-line hard dollar
   -Decreases existing business costs
   -Example: defects, warranty, maintenance, labor, freight
   -Takes cost off the books or adds revenue to the books
-Cost Avoidance
   -Avoids incremental costs that have not been incurred but would have occurred if
      project were not performed
   -Example: enhanced material or changes that would affect warranty work
-Lost Profit Avoidance
   -Avoids lost sales that have not been incurred, but would have occurred if project
      had not occurred
   -Example: a project reduces frequency of line shut downs
-Productivity
   -Increases in productivity which improves utilization of existing resources
   -Example: Redeployment of labor or assets to better use
-Profit Enhancement
   -Potential sales increase, which would increase gross profit
   -Example: Change that was justifiable through a survey, pilots, or assumptions
-Intangible
   -Improvements to operations of business which can be necessary to control, protect,
      and or enhance company assets but are not quantifiable
   -Example: Administrative control process that could result in high legal liability
      expense if not addressed

101

# Chapter 8: Measure

As Jorge looked out the window, he reflected on the Measuring phase of the DMAIC roadmap. It wasn't flashy, but it was a very important part of the five phases because of the significant impact it had on a project outcome. It couldn't be hurried through. You had to develop a reliable and valid measurement system of the business process identified in the Define phase. If you didn't, you could wind up making the wrong kind of improvement efforts and get stuck in firefighting mode.

He thought again of Tom Gorman, the MBB who trained him at Harris. Tom wasn't there anymore – true to his word, he had actually trained himself right out of a job! Ultimately, Jorge reflected, the consultant was only successful at his job when he wasn't needed anymore. That had been a new one on Jorge. Usually, these consultants try to find ways of sticking around as long as they can.

Tom had done his job well. His many years of experience taught Jorge and the others on the $S^4$/IEE team exactly how to interpret the data they collected. For a 30,000-foot-level metric that is shown to be predictable, you could estimate what its expected non-conformance proportion would be; in other words, how far out of whack it's likely to be as it currently operates!

For example, at Harris, they looked at insurance claims. They measured the non-conformance proportion of their process and found that as many as 80% of insurance claims took between one and four months to obtain collection. Numbers like that helped put things into a perspective that the $S^4$/IEE team could understand. It wasn't subjective, it wasn't padded, and it was something that could be measured objectively.

Once the team found a process that was incapable of providing what the internal or external customer wanted, it then went on to develop some improvement strategies. As these strategies were developed, once again the VOC was taken into consideration.

Tom taught them that customers wanted improvements in areas that were critical to four major areas: care, quality, cost, and satisfaction. In order to help the team collect and interpret customer feedback, Tom helped them develop their skills with the Six Sigma and Lean tools that they needed. Jorge still recalled Tom's asking the team questions like, "Who is the customer? What does he/she want? Does our strategy address those needs?"

But the VOC wasn't all Tom had them look at. There was variability to consider, too. The $S^4$/IEE 30,000-foot-level metrics separated common causes of process failure from special causes. It's the special causes that get all the attention subjectively – the big disasters that don't happen often, but when they do, people remember them forever. However, their training taught them that more gains could be made by fixing the common causes so that they didn't reoccur. Special causes were special events that had to be addressed individually; you might even leave these situations alone. You can't gear your process towards conditions that only exist once a year. If you do, you might wind up with more problems than you already have.

Next, Tom had Jorge and the Black Belts do a flowchart and time-value diagram (See Figure 6) of the system, with the width of the bars on the top of the long horizontal line indicating value-added time, and the spaces on the top of the line between vertical bars indicating wasted time, while the width of the bars below the line indicated wasted but necessary time.

Then they brainstormed for any items that could impact the KPOV and searched for improvement opportunities. They ranked these problems according to level of importance, along with conducting a Failure Mode and Effects Analysis (See Table 2).

Once the S⁴/IEE team members had collected all the data they would need, it was time for them to take the next step.

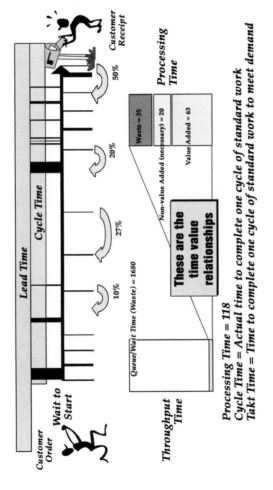

**Figure 6: Time Value Diagram**
From *Implementing Six Sigma*, 2nd edition, with permission.

105

# Table 2: FMEA for ED Admission Order

POTENTIAL
FAILURE MODE AND EFFECTS ANALYSIS

| FMEA Type (Design or Process) | | System | | Project Name/Description: | | | Prepared By: | | | Order Admission | | | Date (Orig.): | | | | | | | |
| --- | --- | --- | --- | --- | --- | --- | --- | --- | --- | --- | --- | --- | --- | --- | --- | --- | --- | --- | --- | --- |
| Responsibility/ | | | | | | | | | | | | | Date (Rev.): | | | | | | | |
| Core Team: | | | | | | | | | | | | | Date (Key): | | | | | | | |
| Design FMEA (Item /Function) Process FMEA (Function/Requirements) | Potential Failure Mode | Potential Effect(s) of Failure | S e v | Potential Cause(s) / Mechanism(s) of Failure | O c c u r | Current Controls | D e t e c | R P N | Recommended Actions | Responsibility & Target Completion Date | Actions Taken | S e v | O c c u r | D e t e c | R P N |
| Dr. Order | Late | Long Wait | 9 | Dr forgot | 3 | None | 9 | 243 | Priority List | | | 5 | 1 | 3 | 15 |
| | | | 9 | Nurse forgot | 3 | None | 9 | 243 | Priority List | | | 5 | 1 | 3 | 15 |
| | | | 9 | Secretary forgot | 3 | None | 9 | 243 | Priority List | | | 5 | 1 | 3 | 15 |
| | Wrong Floor ordered | Transfers | 9 | Wrong order | 3 | None | 9 | 243 | Unit-patient type List | | | 1 | 1 | 1 | 1 |
| | | | 9 | Wrongly called | 5 | None | 9 | 405 | Double check | | | 1 | 1 | 1 | 1 |
| Bed Control | Delayed Decision | Long Wait | 9 | Too busy | 5 | None | 9 | 405 | Proper Staffing | | | 3 | 3 | 1 | 9 |
| | | | 9 | Nurses Delay | 9 | None | 9 | 729 | Adm Nurse | | | 1 | 1 | 1 | 1 |
| | | | 9 | Too many orders | 1 | None | 9 | 81 | Adm Nurse | | | 1 | 1 | 1 | 1 |
| Housekeeping | Delay/ Clean Room | Long wait | 9 | Low priority | 3 | None | 9 | 243 | Discharge Team | | | 1 | 1 | 1 | 1 |
| | | | 9 | Too many orders | 1 | None | 9 | 81 | Discharge Team | | | 1 | 1 | 1 | 1 |
| | | | 9 | Shortage of staff | 3 | Hskp Supervisor | 1 | 27 | none | | | 9 | 3 | 1 | 27 |
| Nursing Unit | Do not accept | Long Wait | 9 | Shortage of staff | 7 | Nursing Sup | 3 | 189 | Proper Staffing | | | 3 | 3 | 3 | 27 |
| | | | 9 | Hide Beds | 7 | None | 9 | 567 | Proper Staffing | | | 3 | 3 | 3 | 27 |
| | | | 9 | Wait till shift end | 7 | None | 9 | 567 | Adm Nurse | | | 1 | 1 | 1 | 1 |

# Chapter 9: Analyze

Jorge left his thinking spot at the window of Sandra's room and walked down the hall to use the restroom. He didn't want to wake his wife until Cliff came around again. As he walked, he recalled the time his $S^4$/IEE team members gathered the Wisdom of the Org and found some low-hanging fruit - the medication error rate. There was something they could do quickly to reduce the likelihood of incorrect medication, and it was so obvious, easy, and cheap that they all agreed to the change – which involved simply redesigning the medication order sheet.

It turned out that the change to the order sheet brought the medication error rate way down – and to prove it, their analyze phase tools measured the statistical significance of the change and statistically quantified its expected impact. Jorge remembered the first time he saw the team's 30,000-foot-level control chart change to a new, improved level of performance – objective, quantifiable proof that they had actually made their process stronger. A new process level was established for Harris that day, and the numbers told them that it was going to make a big impact on bottom line and customer satisfaction, which, more often than not, were interconnected.

Of course, there were other cases where the team needed more information to determine what should be done differently – the "murder mysteries." But, between the functional-hand-off metric system, the Wisdom of the Org, and the Voice of the Customer, $S^4$/IEE always led them to the KPIV that was the culprit.

Tom taught them that it was important to analyze the collected data in a manner that gave insight. He taught them to make statistical assessments as to whether or not apparent differences indicated in the pictures the data gave them were significant.

For example, an issue affecting a unit could be examined to find out if there was a statistically significant difference between $1^{st}$ shift and $2^{nd}$ shift relative to the frequency of the problem. If there were a significant statistical difference between the shifts, $S^4$/IEE would suggest that the focus shouldn't be on what the one shift was doing wrong. Instead, the focus should be on the shift that was doing things right, and the team should be trying to figure out a way to duplicate the best process for the other shift.

Or maybe it's not a shift-wide issue, maybe it's just that the right kind of people aren't being hired to do a particular job. That happened in one case at Harris, and so Jorge got HR involved to help fix the problem. Once the person with the proper qualifications was placed in the position, the process 30,000-foot-level XmR control chart shifted to the better.

# Chapter 10: Improve

Jorge came back to Sandra's room from the bathroom. She was still sleeping. Jorge was unable to worry anymore than he already had. Waiting this long for a specialist wasn't only bad for business; it was dangerous. What if there was a time-sensitive issue that Sandra faced? If the specialists were only available at certain times due to the process within which they worked, Jorge pondered, then could a hospital's process itself be held accountable for negligence if it failed to provide timely care?

Jorge sat back down in the chair by Sandra's bed and, arranging the pillow and blanket Nurse Barnes had given him so long ago, he tried to make himself as comfortable as possible. 4:30 am, the clock on the wall read.

"Won't be long now," thought Jorge. He turned on the TV and checked the news. The same legal experts who had been on hours ago were still debating the same issue. Jorge fell asleep in his chair as though shot with a tranquilizer dart.

In his dream, Jorge was in a meeting with the Black Belts on his team to discuss which KPOVs within the Critical Care unit were not meeting performance standards. They found that the "diagnosis-to-bed" metric was predictable (See Figure 7).

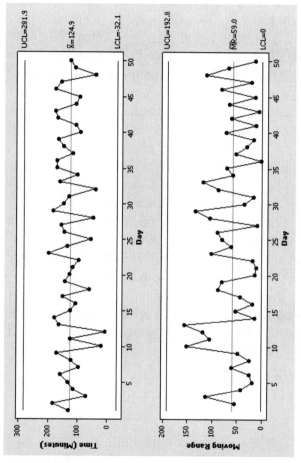

**Figure 7: XmR Chart of Diagnostic to Bed Time (One Sample Selected Daily)**

110

Jorge and the Black Belts then established a numerical goal for the ailing process in the project charter. From their XmR chart they believed that an upper non-conformance goal of thirty minutes was realistic and acceptable from a customer point of view. Next they wanted to determine the process capability/performance metric relative to this upper specification limit (USL) of 30 minutes. Often this is presented as a histogram with a normal probability density function (pdf) overlay (See Figure 8).

From this plot it was obvious that the process was not doing very well; however, it was hard to express the percentage of non-conformance in terms that everyone understood. A probability plot is useful not only to determine if the data was normally distributed, but also to estimate the percentage of nonconformance (See Figure 9).

The data didn't appear to be taken from a population that was normally distributed. There could be more than one input that was affecting the response. An investigation into the cause for this difference could give the Harris team insight into what they could do to improve the process. But, in the short term, they were able to give a rough estimate that, 98% of the time, beds were not filled within 30 minutes of diagnosis.

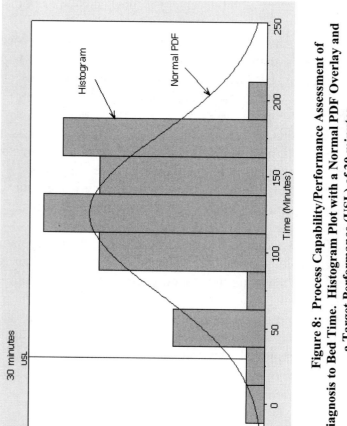

**Figure 8: Process Capability/Performance Assessment of Diagnosis to Bed Time. Histogram Plot with a Normal PDF Overlay and a Target Performance (USL) of 30 minutes**

112

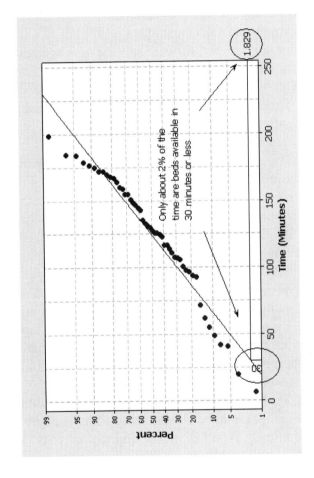

**Figure 9: Normal Probability Plot of Diagnosis to Bed Time**

The team examined the problem, considered the VOC and the Wisdom of the Org, and came up with some ideas, but they needed to be tested. So, they decided to consider some Design of Experiments (DOE) techniques.

Jorge's dream jumped forward in time as Jorge and his Black Belts analyzed the process. Eventually, they came up with the top KPIV issues within that process. They were:

1. The amount of time it took the nurse to admit a patient to a bed
2. Bed not ready
3. The length of time it takes for the patients family to arrive and pick-up the patient so that he can be discharged, and the bed can be "turned over"

Then, the BBs talked in more informed detail about what could be done to meet their goal. The Black Belts got together with their Green Belts and talked about the specifics within the diagnosis-to-bed process. They brainstormed about ways to express a numerical solution to the problem. Tom kept them on track by not allowing them to focus on red tape or other barriers like outdated laws or insurance regulations that could inhibit the process – those were problems they couldn't fix.

Finally, they reached some solutions. After examining their work flow using Lean techniques, with which many of the managers were already familiar, they found that they had a lot of delays in their process. With this data, some changes were made. They began discharge teaching during the admit process – which sped up the discharge process. They also started using a separate discharge process for ED patients with less serious conditions. They created a waiting area for these patients to wait for family members to pick them up, so that beds could be prepared more quickly for new patients.

Also, an examination of work flow processes led to placing needed materials directly in the path of the process, versus randomly placed in the room. Internal steps were converted to external. Tasks that were done as part of the process were converted to tasks that were performed ahead of time or deferred until later. Handoffs were minimized - staff was trained to perform easily-learned tasks and answer questions themselves, rather than having to ask for another staff member or supervisor to intervene.

In Jorge's dream, a Green Belt at Harris by the name of Larry Hass gave him the same boggled look as he himself wore in the conference room with Tom Gorman over two years earlier, "Do you know what it will cost to train all those people and implement all these changes? The hospital will never go for it!" he predicted.

"Sure they will," one of his Black Belts had offered in defense of the team's recommendations. "With guys like our Jorge over here backing us, we can get whatever we need!"

It was that same Larry who later suggested that they install medication management bedside devices to help eliminate medication errors – a bold suggestion they wound up following.

They also set up a system where patients would be "pulled" from Triage to the Critical Care Unit. The initial call from Triage, notifying CCU of an incoming patient, was designed to trigger a chain of events that eventually led to the patient being transported to CCU by CCU staff. By using a tool to measure demand over time, they found that 50 percent of ER patients were admitted within two hours of being seen by a doctor. ICU was then able to anticipate the demand for a bed, and have one ready as soon as an Emergency Department patient needed it. (See Figure 10)

A dot plot of the data before and after the change indicates improvements were made; however, the 30 minute specification was still often not met (See Figure 11).

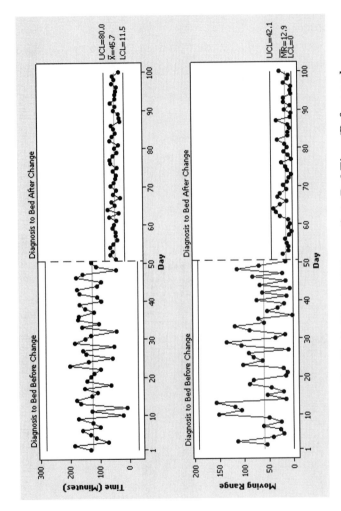

**Figure 10: XmR Chart of Diagnostic to Bed Time (Before and After Change)**

117

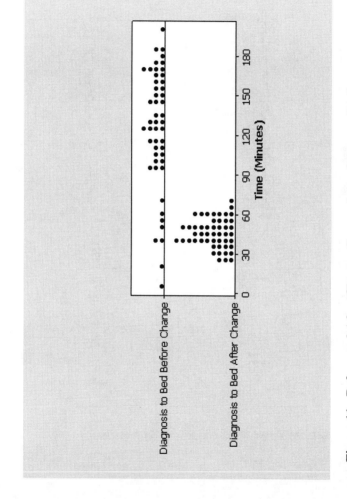

**Figure 11: Before and After Change Comparison of Process Performance**

118

In his dream, Jorge began tossing and turning a little as he remembered what they did in order to extend the time of the much-demanded Specialists. One thing they did was to have them perform only the tasks that demanded their specific skills. They matched the physicians' schedules with patient need. Some other changes to the system they made had to do with educating patients during waiting times and scheduling routine care at low-demand times.

When Jorge's team members were done with the Improvement phase of the projects, they calculated that they had saved the hospital approximately 500,000 dollars per project – in addition to the added benefit of improved customer satisfaction. Everyone on the team felt good. They didn't just tell staff to do their job better; they gave them the tools to make it happen. Not only that, but they all had the sense that running successful projects like this one would not be bad for their careers!

# Chapter 11: Control

It was 5:30 a.m., and the specialists could arrive any minute. Sandra was awake in her bed and only slightly groggy. The sleep had done a world of good for her. She was still banged up and swollen, and still heavily medicated, but to Jorge, her eyes seemed more alive this morning. He was in the chair next to her, reading her the paper and sipping coffee.

Sandra appreciated the way that he was staying strong for her, as though she had nothing at all to worry about. She knew he was worried, though. The bags under his eyes told the story.

She interrupted the newspaper article he was reading to her about how the city wanted to raise property taxes again.

"Jorge?"

"Yes, can I get you something?"

"Did you ever finish telling me about your project at the hospital?"

"Well, no, I didn't. I suppose you want to hear it?"

"Un hm."

"You can't go to sleep on me again. The doctors will be here soon."

"No," Sandra said, "I really want to know. What did you do to make sure that the gains your team made weren't lost after you left the Emergency Department project?"

Jorge shook his head slowly as something occurred to him. "You know something," he said, "I think somebody's been listening in on the old *Professor* from time to time when he's been holding class with his friends."

"Whatever do you mean?" Sandra said innocently.

Jorge wagged a finger at her, "Wait a second...I'm on to you now, young lady. You wouldn't have gotten a business degree in college if you didn't like business. You could have gotten an arts degree or something. Confess. You find this Six Sigma stuff interesting, don't you?"

Sandra managed a feeble smile. "Maybe I overheard a few conversations," she admitted.

"And all this time you acted like Six Sigma was the last thing you wanted to hear about!"

"I was trying to keep you humble," she said, "but now that I see there's no hope for that, I might as well come clean. I really think that this type of Six Sigma should be taught in business schools as a mandatory topic. Seems to me that MBAs could really benefit from it!"

"Ha!" Jorge said.

"Well then, *Professor*. Are you going to tell me how you kept those gains or not?"

Jorge was grinning ear to ear, "Well, how about that?" he asked rhetorically, "Sure, sure I'll tell you, as long as we've obviously got a few moments to spare here. I think we'll be lucky if these specialists show up before lunch."

"Jorge, don't be nasty."

"You're right. I'm sorry. So, to answer your question, there were a number of things we did in order to make sure that we didn't lose the gains we made. First of all, we documented the optimum process settings, conditions, and KPIVs. Then, we came up with ways to keep the process in control, which is called a 'control plan'. This includes all our 50–foot-level charts, so that the moment a process input goes out of whack, the managers know what to do to fix it. We also included the 30,000-foot-level metrics within the process owner's performance plan."

"So," Sandra said, "you turned the process back over to the managers at some point?"

"That's right, after the financial officers completed their financial validation of the process improvements. Then, once we had the results of the project in hand, and we could prove the benefits of what we did, we then leveraged those results in other areas of the hospital. That way, everyone has access to the information, just in case it can help them in their departments. For example, many of the departments could lower their medication inventory after we got the prescription supply store to open next door to the hospital for the 'inventory reduction' project we ran in the Emergency Department. As Tom told us, there's no need for every hospital to reinvent the wheel, and also no need for every department to reinvent it either."

"Then," Jorge finished, "we always check back in a few months to make sure the improvements have been maintained."

"So, Mr. Kung Fu hot shot," Sandra teased him, which Jorge thought was remarkable considering her condition, "you said you measured the benefits of the projects you ran in the Emergency Department?"

"That's right."

"Well, what were they?"

"Well, how does a 4.5 million per year cost reduction, with a 40% decrease in the average patient Length of Stay sound?"

"Wow!"

"Also, beds were ready much faster, and patients were moved to inpatient beds much more quickly. Speaking of which, and I hate to say it, but those are some cues this hospital could stand to take from Harris. It took forever to get you into a bed after your surgery. And waiting overnight for the specialists to arrive hasn't been any picnic either."

"Well, we do what we can," said a dry, unfamiliar voice from the doorway of Sandra's room.

Jorge turned in surprise to watch two doctors enter, who Jorge could only assume were the long awaited neurosurgeon and cardiovascular specialist.

# Chapter 12: Conclusion

After Jorge recovered from his embarrassment, the specialists introduced themselves as Drs. Thompson and Kader. They then proceeded to examine Sandra and ask her a number of questions. As they examined her, the trauma surgeon, Dr. Miller, and the plastic surgeon, Dr. Monk, also entered the room and made their own examinations of Sandra. Jorge found it strange that none of them had been there for so long, and now they were all there at once. However, the last thing he was going to do was question the efficiency of their system twice in ten minutes – at least, not until Sandra was out of the hospital!

When they were finished with their examination, the doctors all seemed satisfied that she was on track for a full recovery in time.

"Thank you," Jorge said as they reported their positive prognosis to him and Sandra. "I really appreciate everything you've done."

"Yes, thank you," Sandra told them.

"Oh, there's no need for that," Dr. Kader said.

"Not at all," Dr. Miller chimed in, "especially not from a bigwig over at Harris Hospital."

"Oh," Dr. Thompson joined in, "so this is *the* Jorge Santos, efficiency guru."

Jorge felt flustered, surrounded as he was by the doctors in their business suits and white lab coats.

"How can you all possibly know who I am?" he asked.

The doctors all chuckled and Dr. Miller spilled the beans. "My husband is Dr. Miller from Harris Hospital, in the Emergency Department?"

"Kareem Miller?"

"Yes. He told me about you back when your $S^4$/IEE team swooped in and reorganized the whole department. He couldn't say enough about how much more smoothly everything ran after you were through."

"Wow," Jorge said, "that's really gratifying to hear. Thank you."

"I'm surprised you don't hear it all the time," Dr. Miller said, "and actually, I'd like to thank you. Since then, Kareem's been a lot happier in his job, really doing the things he was trained for and loves, instead of wading through tasks that could be done by somebody else. He's like a different person when he comes home from work now."

"Hey," Dr. Kader piped in, "maybe you could work some of that magic around here."

"I'll second that," Dr. Thompson added.

"Oh no," Sandra said from the bed, "he's got to take care of me first."

They all laughed.

"Well, I guess we can wait a little while," Dr. Monk said, "but as soon as you're done with him, we'd like *Doctor* Santos here to come work with us for a while. Deal?"

Sandra shot Jorge a look as if she knew exactly what was going through his head.

And she did. It was:

Hmm…first *Professor* Jorge, now *Doctor* Santos. Now that's a title I think I could get used to!

# List of Symbols

| | |
|---|---|
| AD | Anderson-Darling (test for normality) |
| ANOVA | Analysis of variance |
| ANOM | Analysis of means |
| AQL | Acceptable quality level |
| ASQ | American Society for Quality |
| BB | Black Belt |
| CCU | Critical care unit |
| COPQ | Cost of poor quality |
| CODND | Cost of doing nothing different |
| CTQ | Critical to quality |
| CUSUM | Cumulative sum (control chart approach) |
| DFSS | Design for six sigma |
| DOE | Design of experiments |
| DPMO | Defects per million opportunities |
| ED | Emergency department |
| EPC | Engineering process control |
| ER | Emergency room |
| EVOP | Evolutionary operation |
| EWMA | Exponentially weighted moving average |
| HR | Human Resource |
| ICU | Intensive Care Unit |
| KPIV | Key Process Input Variable |
| KPOV | Key Process Output Variable |
| LOS | Length of stay |
| LCL | Lower control limit |
| LSL | Lower specification limit |
| MBB | Master Black Belt |
| MSA | Measurement systems analysis |
| N | Sample size |
| OR | Operating room |
| PACU | Post-Anesthesia Care Unit |
| PDF | Probability density function |
| PM | Project management |
| $R$ | Range |

| | |
|---|---|
| RPN | Risk priority number |
| $s$ | Standard deviation of a sample |
| StDev | Standard deviation of a sample |
| TAT | Turn around time |
| TOC | Theory of constraints |
| TQM | Total quality management |
| VOC | Voice of the customer |
| UCL | Upper control limit |
| USL | Upper specification limit |
| XmR | X (individuals) moving range |
| $\bar{x}$ | Sample mean |
| $\mu$ | Mu, population true mean |
| $\sigma$ | Sigma, population standard deviation |

# Glossary[4]

$2^k$ **DOE**: Each of the $k$ factors in a DOE has two levels.

**Analysis of means (ANOM):** A statistical procedure to compare means of groups of common size to the grand mean.

**Analysis of variance (ANOVA):** A statistical procedure that can be used to determine statistical significance when an output is continuous and there are discrete levels of the input.

**Attribute data (Discrete data):** The presence or absence of some characteristic in each device under test (e.g., proportion nonconforming in a pass/fail test).

**Average:** See Mean.

**Benchmarking:** To provide a standard against which something can be assessed.

**Best estimate:** A value where there is a 50% chance that the true reading is higher/lower than the estimate.

**Bimodal distribution:** A distribution that is a combination of two different distributions resulting in two distinct peaks.

**Bottom-Line:** The final profit or loss that a company experiences at the end of a given period of time.

**Box plot:** Describes various aspects of data pictorially. The box contains the lower and upper quartiles. The median appears as a horizontal line within the box. It is sometimes called a box-and-whisker plot.

**Brainstorming:** Consensus building among experts about a problem or issue using group discussion.

**Capability, Process:** See Process capability.

**Chi-square analysis:** An analysis that uses the chi-square statistic. A chi-square analysis would be an appropriate hypothesis statistic that tests the equality of failure rates from multiple sources within a process; e.g., machine or inspector failure rates.

---

[4] Subset of glossary definitions from *Implementing Six Sigma*, 2nd edition, with permission

**Common Causes:** Faults of the system are common causes of trouble (Deming 1986).

**Control plan**: A written document created to ensure that processes are run so that products or services meet or exceed customer requirements at all times. It should be a living document, which is updated with both additions and deletions of controls based on experience from the process.

**Confidence interval:** The region containing the limits or band of a parameter with an associated confidence level that the bounds are large enough to contain the true parameter value. The bands can be single-sided to describe an upper/lower limit or double sided to describe both upper and lower limits.

**Continuous data** (Variables data): Data that can assume a range of numerical responses on a continuous scale, as opposed to data that can assume only discrete levels.

**Continuous data response:** See Response.

**Control chart:** A procedure used to track a process with time for the purpose of determining if common or special causes exist.

**Control:** The term "in control" or predictable is used in process control charting to describe when the process indicates that there are no special causes. "Out of control" indicates that there is a special cause or the process is unpredictable.

**Correlation coefficient ($r$):** A statistic that describes the strength of a relationship between two variables is the sample correlation coefficient. A correlation coefficient can take values between -1 and +1. A -1 indicates perfect negative correlation, while a +1 indicates perfect positive correlation. A zero indicates no correlation.

**Cost of doing nothing differently (CODND):** COPQ within Six Sigma includes not doing what is right the first time, which can encompass issues such as scrap, reworks, and meetings with no purpose. To keep $S^4/IEE$ from appearing as a quality initiative, it can be beneficial to reference this metric; i.e., the cost of doing nothing differently (CODND), which has even broader costing implications than COPQ.

**Cost of poor quality (COPQ):** Traditionally cost of quality issues have been given the broad categories of internal failure costs, external failure costs, appraisal costs, and prevention costs.

129

**Cumulative distribution function (CDF) [$F(x)$]:** The calculated integral of the PDF from minus infinity to $x$. This integration takes on a characteristic "percentage less than or percentile" when plotted against $x$.

**Customer:** Someone for whom work or a service is performed. The end user of a product is a customer of the employees within a company that manufactures the product. There are also internal customers in a company. When an employee does work or performs a service for someone else in the company, the person who receives this work is a customer of this employee.

**Cycle Time:** Frequency that a part/product is completed by process. Also, time it takes for operator to go through work activities before repeating the activities. In addition, cycle time can be used to quantify customer order to delivery time.

**Defect:** A nonconformity or departure of a quality characteristic from its intended level or state.

**Defective:** A nonconforming item that contains at least one defect, or having a combination of several imperfections causing the unit not to satisfy intended requirements.

**Descriptive statistics** Descriptive statistics help pull useful information from data, whereas probability provides among other things a basis for inferential statistics and sampling plans.

**Design for Six Sigma (DFSS):** A structured approach that can utilize both six sigma and lean tools within the development process for both product and processes. DFSS can lead to a significant reduction in development cycle time and likelihood of reworks, while maximizing customer satisfaction.

**Discrete data (Attribute data):** The presence or absence of some characteristic in each device under test (e.g., proportion nonconforming in a pass/fail test).

**DMAIC:** Define-Measure-Analyze-Improve-Control Six Sigma roadmap.

**Distribution:** A pattern that randomly collected numbers from a population follows. The normal, Weibull, Poisson, binomial, and log-normal distributions are applicable to the modeling of various industrial situations.

**DPMO:** When using the non-conformance rate calculation of defects per million opportunities (DPMO) one needs to first describe what the opportunities for defects are in the process; e.g., the number of components and solder joints when manufacturing printed circuit boards. Next the number of defects is periodically divided by the number of opportunities to determine the DMPO rate.

**Failure:** A device is said to fail when it no longer performs its intended function satisfactorily.

**Failure mode and effects analysis (FMEA):** Analytical approach directed toward problem prevention through the prioritization of potential problems and their resolution. Opposite of fault tree analysis.

**Failure rate:** Failures/unit time or failures/units of usage. Sample failure rates are: 0.002 failures/hour, 0.0003 failures/auto miles traveled, 0.01 failures/1000 parts manufactured.

**Fire fighting**: An expression used to describe the process of performing emergency fixes to problems.

**50-Foot Level:** A low-level view of a KPIV metric; e.g., process temperature when manufacturing plastic parts. This type of chart can involve frequent sampling since special cause issues need timely identification so that problems can be quickly resolved without jeopardizing the quality or timeliness of the outgoing product or service.

**5S**: A basic housekeeping discipline for both the shop floor and office (sort, straighten, shine, standardize, sustain).

**Functional-hand-off metric system:** An organizational enterprise consists of processes and sub-processes that should align and support the overall objective of the enterprise; e.g., more customers and cash. Within these processes and sub-processes there are outputs and functional supplier-customer relationships. A functional-hand-off metric system tracks and reports the KPOVs of these hand-offs at the 30,000-foot-level. Functional-hand-off metrics should be in the process owner's performance plan.

**Gage repeatability and reproducibility (R&R) study:** The evaluation of measuring instruments to determine capability to yield a precise response. Gage repeatability is the variation in measurements considering one part and one operator. Gage reproducibility is the variation between operators measuring one part.

**Hard savings:** Savings that directly impact the bottom-line.

**Histogram:** A graphical representation of the sample frequency distribution that describes the occurrence of grouped items.

**Hypothesis testing:** Consists of a null hypothesis $(H_0)$ and alternative hypothesis $(H_a)$ where, for example, a null hypothesis indicates equality between two process outputs and an alternative hypothesis indicates non-equality. Through a hypothesis test a decision is made whether to reject a null hypothesis or not reject a null hypothesis. When a null hypothesis is rejected, there is $\alpha$ risk of error. Most typically there is no risk assignment when we fail to reject the null hypothesis. However, an appropriate sample size could be determined such that failure to reject the null hypothesis is made with $\beta$ risk of error.

**Incapable process:** A process that does not produce results consistently with specification requirements or customer expectations.

**In control:** The description of a process where variation is consistent over time (i.e., only common causes exist). The process is predictable.

**Inferential statistics:** From the analysis of samples we can make statements about the population using inferential statistics. That is, properties of the population are inferred from the analysis of samples.

**Infrequent sub-grouping/sampling:** Traditionally, rational sub-grouping issues involve the selection of samples that yield relatively homogeneous conditions within the subgroup for a small region of time or space, perhaps five in a row. For a given situation, differing sub-grouping methodologies can dramatically affect the measured variation within subgroups, which in turn affects the width of the control limits. For the high-level metrics of $S^4$/IEE we want infrequent sub-grouping/sampling so that short-term variations caused by KPIV perturbations are viewed as common cause issues. A 30,000 Foot-Level XmR chart created with infrequent sub-grouping/sampling can reduce the amount of fire fighting in an organization. However, this does not mean a problem does not exist within the process. When process capability/performance improvements are needed for these metrics we can initiate an $S^4$/IEE project; i.e., $S^4$/IEE projects are pulled (using a Lean term) into the system, as they are needed by the metrics.

**Integrated Enterprise Excellence (IEE, I double E):** A roadmap for the creation of an enterprise system in which organizations can significantly improve both customer satisfaction and their bottom-line. The techniques help manufacturing, development, and service organizations become more competitive and/or move them to new heights. IEE is a structured approach that guides organizations through the tracking and attainment of

132

organizational goals. This is accomplished through the wise implementation of traditional Six Sigma techniques and other methodologies -- throughout the whole enterprise of an organization. IEE goes well beyond traditional Six Sigma methods to an enhanced version of the $S^4$ method described in the first edition *Implementing Six Sigma*. With this enhanced version of $S^4$ we integrate enterprise measures and improvement methodologies with tools such as Lean and Theory of Constraints (TOC) in a never ending pursuit of excellence. This enhanced version of $S^4$ also serves to integrate, improve, and align with other initiatives such as Total Quality Management (TQM), ISO 9000, Malcolm Baldrige Assessments and the Shingo Prize.

**Lean:** Improving operations and the supply chain with an emphasis for the reduction of wasteful activities like waiting, transportation, material hand-offs, inventory, and overproduction.

**Marginal plot:** Permits the visualization of the distribution of data in both the $x$ and $y$ direction.

**Mean:** The mean of a sample ($\bar{x}$) is the sum of all the responses divided by the sample size. The mean of a population ($\mu$) is the sum of all responses of the population divided by the population size. In a random sample of a population, $\bar{x}$ is an estimate of the $\mu$ of the population.

**Measurement systems analysis (MSA):** Assessment of the overall measurement system, including Gage repeatability and reproducibility (R&R).

**Median:** For a sample the number that is in the middle when all observations are ranked in magnitude. For a population the value at which the cumulative distribution function is 0.5.

**Multi-vari chart:** A graphic that allows visual decomposition into components and the identification of the component that affects variability the most.

**Normal distribution:** A bell-shaped distribution that is often useful to describe various physical, mechanical, electrical, and chemical properties.

**Null hypothesis:** See hypothesis

**Orming model:** Tuckman (1965) described the four stages of team development as forming, storming, norming, and performing. These stages are often referenced as the orming model.

**Out of Control:** Control charts exhibiting special cause(s) conditions. The process is not predictable.

**Pareto chart:** A graphical technique used to quantify problems so that effort can be expended in fixing the "vital few" causes, as opposed to the "trivial many." Named after Vilfredo Pareto, an Italian economist.

**Pareto principle:** 80% of the trouble comes from 20% of the problems (i.e., the vital few problems).

**Pass/fail functional testing:** A methodology that uses DOE matrices to design an efficient test of a pass/fail logic response for multiple combinational considerations.

**Passive analysis:** In $S^4$/IEE and a traditional DMAIC, most Six Sigma tools are applied in the same phase. However, the term "passive analysis" is often used in $S^4$/IEE to more descriptively describe the analyze phase, where process data are observed passively (i.e., with no process adjustments) in an attempt to find a causal relationship between input and output variables. It should be noted that *improvements* can be made in any of the phases. If there is low hanging fruit identified during a brainstorming session in the measure phase, this improvement can be made immediately, which could yield a dramatic improvement to the 30,000 Foot-Level output metric.

**Point estimate:** An estimate calculated from sample data without a confidence interval.

**Poka-yoke:** A poka-yoke device is a mechanism that either prevents a mistake from occurring or makes a mistake obvious at a glance.

**Population:** The totality of items under consideration.

**Pre-control chart:** An approach to monitor processes over time which involves the classification of product measurements into one of three groups depending upon the relative position of the measurement to specification limits. The process is to be adjusted when certain patterns occur in the plot.

**Probability plot:** Data are plotted on a selected probability paper coordinate system to determine if a particular distribution is appropriate (i.e., the data plots as a straight line) and to make statements about percentiles of the population.

**Problem solving:** The process of determining the cause from a symptom and then choosing an action to improve a process or product.

**Process:** A method to make or do something that involves a number of steps.

**Process capability indices ($C_p$ and $C_{pk}$):** $C_p$ is a measurement of the allowable tolerance spread divided by the actual $6\sigma$ data spread. $C_{pk}$ has a similar ratio to that of $C_p$ except that this ratio considers the shift of the mean relative to the central specification target.

**Process capability:** AIAG (1995) definition for the variables data case is $6\sigma$ range of a process's inherent variation; for statistically stable processes, where $\sigma$ is usually estimated by $\overline{R}/d_2$. For the attribute data case it is usually defined as the average proportion or rate of defects or defectives; e.g., center of an attribute control chart.

**Process performance:** The AIAG (1995) definition is the $6\sigma$ range of a process's total variation, where $\sigma$ is usually estimated by $s$, the sample standard deviation.

**Process flow diagram (chart):** Path of steps of work used to produce or do something.

**Pull:** A Lean term that results in an activity when a customer or downstream process step requests the activity. A homebuilder that builds houses only when an agreement is reach on the sale of the house is using a pull system. *See push.*

**Push:** A Lean term that results in an activity that a customer or downstream process step has not specifically requested. This activity can create excessive waste and/or inventory. A homebuilder that builds houses on the speculation of sale is using a push system. If the house does not sell promptly upon completion, the homebuilder has created excess inventory for his company, which can be very costly. *See pull.*

**p-value:** A statistical analysis output. The null hypothesis is rejected when this value is equal to or less than the desired level of significance; e.g. 0.05.

**Qualitative factor:** A factor that has discrete levels. For example, product origination where the factor levels are supplier A, supplier B, and supplier C.

**Quantitative factor:** A factor that is continuous. For example, a product can be manufactured with a process temperature factor between 50°C and 80°C.

**Random:** Having no specific pattern.

**Range:** For a set of numbers, the absolute difference between the largest and smallest value.

**Regression analysis:** Data collected from an experiment are used to empirically quantify through a mathematical model the relationship that exists between the response variable and influencing factors. In a simple linear regression model, $y = b_0 + b_1x + \varepsilon$, $x$ is the regressor, $y$ is the expected response, $b_0$ and $b_1$ are coefficients, and $\varepsilon$ is random error.

**Reliability:** The proportion surviving at some point in time during the life of a device. Can also be a generic description of tests which are conducted to evaluate failure rates.

**Response:** We will consider three basic types of responses (i.e., outputs): continuous (variables), attribute (discrete), and logic pass/fail. A response is said to be continuous if any value can be taken between limits (e.g., 2, 2.0001, and 3.00005). A response is said to be attribute if the evaluation takes on a pass/fail proportion output (e.g., 999 out of 1000 sheets of paper on the average can be fed through a copier without a jam). In this book a response is said to be logic pass/fail if combinational considerations are involved that are said to either always cause an event to pass or fail (e.g., a computer display design will not work in combination with a particular keyboard design and software package).

**Response surface methodology (RSM):** The empirical study of relationships between one or more responses and input variable factors. The technique is used to determine the "best" set of input variables to optimize a response and/or gain a better understanding of the overall system response.

**Risk priority number (RPN):** Product of severity, occurrence, and detection rankings within an FMEA. The ranking of RPN prioritizes design concerns; however, issues with a low RPN still deserve special attention if the severity ranking is high.

**Rolled throughput yield (RTY):** For a process that has a series of steps, RTY is the product of yields for each step.

**Robust:** A description of a procedure that is not sensitive to deviations from some of its underlying assumptions.

**Sample:** A selection of items from a population.

**Sampling distribution:** A distribution derived from a parent distribution by random sampling.

**Satellite-Level:** Used to describe a high level business metric that has infrequent sub-grouping/sampling such that short-term variations, which might be cause by KPIVs, will result in charts that view these perturbations as common cause issues.

**Scatter plot**: Assessment of the relationship between two continuous variables with the intention of determining a cause-and-effect relationship.

**Sigma**: The Greek letter ($\sigma$) that is often used to describe the standard deviation of data.

**Sigma level or sigma quality level**: A quality that is calculated by some to describe the capability of a process to meet specification. A six sigma quality level is said to have a 3.4 ppm rate.

**Significance**: A statistical statement indicating that the level of a factor causes a difference in a response with a certain degree of risk of being in error.

**Six Sigma**: A term coined by Motorola that emphasizes the improvement of processes for the purpose of reducing variability and making general improvements.

**Smarter Six Sigma Solutions (S$^4$)**: Term used within this book to describe the *wise* and often unique application of statistical techniques to creating meaningful measurements and effective improvements.

**Smarter Six Sigma Solutions assessment (S$^4$ assessment)**: Using statistically based concepts while determining the "best" question to answer from the point of view of the customer. Assessment is made to determine if the right measurements and the right actions are being conducted. This includes noting that there are usually better questions to ask (to protect the "customer") than "What sample do I need?" or "What one thing should I do next to fix this problem?" (i.e., a one-at-a-time approach). S$^4$/IEE resolution may involve putting together what often traditionally are considered "separated statistical techniques" in a "smart" fashion to address various problems.

**Soft savings**: Savings that do not directly impact the financial statement; i.e., hard savings. Possible soft savings categories are cost avoidance, lost profit avoidance, productivity improvements, profit enhancement, and other intangibles.

**Soft skills**: A person who effectively facilitates meetings and works well with other people has good soft skills.

**Special causes**: Faults from fleeting events (Deming 1986).

**Specification:** A criterion that is to be met by a part or product.

**Stability:** Refers to both statistical stability of measurement process and measurement stability over time. Both are vital for a measurement system to be adequate for its intended purpose. Statistical stability implies a predictable, underlying measurement process operating within common cause variation. Measurement (alias drift) addresses the necessary conformance to the measurement standard or reference over the operating life (time) of the measurement system. (AIAG 2002)

**Stakeholders:** Those people who are key to the success of an $S^4$/IEE project; e.g., finance, managers, people who are working in the process, upstream/downstream departments, suppliers, and customers.

**Standard deviation ($\sigma$, s):** A mathematical quantity that describes the variability of a response. It equals the square root of variance. The standard deviation of a sample ($s$) is used to estimate the standard deviation of a population ($\sigma$).

**Statistical process control (SPC):** The application of statistical techniques in the control of processes. SPC is often considered a subset of SQC, where the emphasis in SPC is on the tools associated with the process but not product acceptance techniques.

**Taguchi considerations**: An $S^4$/IEE implementation of Genichi Taguchi's philosophy relative to experimentation that leads to the reduction of variability in a process' response.

**Test:** Assessment of whether an item meets specified requirements by subjecting the item to a set of physical, environmental, chemical, or operating actions/conditions.

**30,000-Foot-Level**: A Six Sigma KPOV, CTQ, or $Y$ variable response that is used in $S^4$/IEE to describe a high level project or operation metric that has infrequent sub-grouping/sampling such that short-term variations, which might be cause by KPIVs, will result in charts that view these perturbations as common cause issues. A 30,000-Foot-Level XmR chart can reduce the amount of fire fighting in an organization when used to report operational metrics.

**Theory of constraints:** The TOC described by Goldratt (1992) presents a system thinking process where the focus is on the system's bottlenecks. This result in continual improvement of the performance of the entire system, rather than viewing the system in terms of discrete processes, TOC addresses the larger systematic picture as a chain or grid of inter-linked chains. The performance of the whole chain is determined by the performance of its weakest link

**TRIZ**: Theory of inventive problem solving approach which stresses that an ideal design solution overcomes conflict, as opposed to making a trade-off.

**Value added (VA) time:** The execution time for the work elements that a customer is willing to pay for.

**Value stream mapping:** At Toyota value stream mapping is know as "material and information flow mapping." In the Toyota Production System current and future states/ideal states are depicted by practitioners when they are developing plans to install Lean systems. Infinite attention is given to establishing flow, eliminating waste, and adding value. Toyota view manufacturing flows as material, information and people/process. The described value stream mapping covers the first two of these three items. (Rother and Shook 1999)

**Variables data (Continuous data):** Data that can assume a range of numerical responses on a continuous scale, as opposed to data that can assume only discrete levels.

**Variables:** Factors within a fractional factorial designed experiment or response surface experiment.

**Variance ($\sigma^2$, $s^2$):** A measure of dispersion of observations based upon the mean of the squared deviations from the arithmetic mean.

**Variance components**: A random-effects model that assesses the variability of key process input variables on the variability of key process outputs.

**Visual factory**: Management by sight. Involves the collection and display of real-time information to the entire workforce on a continuing basis. Work cell bulletin boards and other easily seen media might report information about orders, production schedules, quality, deliver performance, and financial health of business.

**Waste:** Seven elements to consider for the elimination of muda, or waste, are correction, overproduction, processing, conveyance, inventory, motion, and waiting.

**Weibull distribution**: A flexible distribution, which can describe many types of data. In the Weibull equation, the shape parameter defines the PDF shape. The scale or characteristic life parameter is the 63.2 percentile point.

**XmR control charts**: A control chart of individual values is typically referred to as an I chart or an X chart. A moving range chart often accompanies these charts; hence, the designation I-MR or XmR chart. The MR chart is a control chart that typically tracks the moving range of adjacent data points.

# References

AIAG (2002), Automotive Industry Action Group, *Measurement Systems Analysis (MSA) Reference Manual*, Third Edition, Chrysler Corporation, Ford Motor Company, General Motors Corporation.

AIAG (1995), *Statistical Process Control (SPC) Reference Manual*, Third edition, Chrysler Corporation, Ford Motor Company, General Motors Corporation.

Breyfogle, F. W. (2003), *Implementing Six Sigma*, 2nd ed., Wiley, New York.

Breyfogle, F. W. (1992), *Statistical Methods for Testing, Development, and Manufacturing*, Wiley, New York.

Breyfogle, F. W., Cupello, J. M., Meadows, B (2001a) *Managing Six Sigma: A Practical Guide to Understanding, Assessing, and Implementing the Strategy that Yields Bottom-Line Success*, Wiley, New York.

Breyfogle, F. W., Enck, D., Flories, P, and Pearson, T. (2001b), *Wisdom on the Green: Smarter Six Sigma Business Solutions,* Smarter Solutions Inc., Austin, TX.

Deming, W. Edwards (1986), *Out of the Crisis*, Massachusetts Institute of Technology, Cambridge, MA.

Goldratt, E. M. (1992), *The Goal*, 2nd ed., North River Press, New York.

Rother, M and Shook, J, (1999), *Learning to See: Value Stream Mapping to Create Value and Eliminate Muda*, The Lean Enterprise Institute, Brookline, MA.

Tuckman, B. W. (1965), Developmental Sequence in Small Groups, *Psychological Bulletin*, Vol. 63, No 6, p. 384-399.

# About the Authors

## Forrest Breyfogle

Forrest Breyfogle is president and CEO of Smarter Solutions, Inc. (*See* About Smarter Solutions section of this book). Mr. Breyfogle, is a Professional Engineer and an ASQ fellow. He is on the board of directors for the University of Texas Center for Performing Excellence. He is the author or co-author of six books on Six Sigma and Lean. One of these books is a primary reference for ASQ's Black Belt certification test. Mr. Breyfogle has been interviewed by several TV, radio, and publications about the application of Six Sigma. For example, he was interviewed by CNNfn and CNBC *Power Lunch*. Mr. Breyfogle has conducted lectures, training, and coaching internationally in the wise application of Six Sigma, Lean, and Balanced Scorecard reporting/metrics. This work has encompassed development, transactional, and manufacturing process in virtually every industry sector, including health care, insurance, food, pharmaceutical, technology, transportation, communications, energy, aviation, chemical, financial, and automotive.

## Arvind Salvekar, Ph.D.

Arvind Salvekar has a Ph. D. in industrial engineering and has been providing process improvement to healthcare for about 35 years. He has conducted Six Sigma training in healthcare for the last three years. He is a Fellow of Health Management Systems Society, Senior Member of IIE, and a Member of ASQ.

# About Smarter Solutions, Inc.

www.SmarterSolutions.com
info@SmarterSolutions.com
7000 N. Mopac Expressway, Suite 200
Austin, TX 78731
512-918-0280

Forrest W. Breyfogle III founded Smarter Solutions in 1992 after a 24-year career at IBM. Mr. Breyfogle began his career with IBM as an engineer in development and later transferred to a product test organization. Within these organizations, he became very interested in the benefits resulting from the wise use of statistical techniques. In 1980, Mr. Breyfogle requested that a full-time position be created for him within IBM as an internal statistical consultant. From 1980 to 1992 Mr. Breyfogle served IBM in this capacity, applying Six Sigma methodology to testing, development, manufacturing, and service organizations.

Mr. Breyfogle has authored or co-authored *Statistical Methods for Testing, Development, and Manufacturing*, Wiley, 1992, *Implementing Six Sigma*, Wiley, 1999, and *Managing Six Sigma*, Wiley, 2001, *Wisdom on the Green*, Smarter Solutions, 2001. *Implementing Six Sigma*, Wiley, 2003.

Mr. Breyfogle's first book, *Statistical Methods for Testing, Development, and Manufacturing*, was written to illustrate the benefits and how-tos of *wisely* applied statistical methodologies. This book, published in 1992, includes a 10-step Six Sigma implementation roadmap.

Mr. Breyfogle and the Smarter Solutions, Inc. team have conducted many Six Sigma workshop sessions throughout the world. On-site and public training/coaching sessions include Master Black Belt, Black Belt, Design for Six Sigma (DFSS), Lean, Green Belt, Yellow Belt, Champion, and Executive training sessions. They have coached many individuals and organizations on the wise application of Six Sigma techniques. In 2001 Mr. Breyfogle was selected as the Six Sigma Subject Matter Expert (SME) for a Six Sigma Benchmarking study orchestrated by APQC.

Members of the Smarter Solutions team are proud of the feedback that they have received on their training and training material, which is made robust to differences that occur in the experience of both workshop attendees and instructors.